# Pascal's Triangle

1

1 1

1 2 1

1 3 3 1

1 4 6 4 1

1 5 10 10 5 1

___ ___ ___ ___ ___ ___ ___

___ ___ ___ ___ ___ ___ ___ ___

# Field Properties of Addition and Multiplication of Real Numbers

For any real numbers $a$, $b$, and $c$:

| | **Addition** | **Multiplication** |
|---|---|---|
| Closure: | $a + b$ is a real number | $ab$ is a real number |
| Commutative: | $a + b = b + a$ | $ab = ba$ |
| Associative: | $a + (b + c) = (a + b) + c$ | $a(bc) = (ab)c$ |
| Identity: | There is a number 0 with $a + 0 = 0 + a = a$ | There is a number $1 \neq 0$ with $a \cdot 1 = 1 \cdot a = a$ |
| Inverse: | There is a number $-a$ with $a + -a = -a + a = 0$ | If $a \neq 0$, there is a number $\frac{1}{a}$ with $a \cdot \frac{1}{a} = \frac{1}{a} \cdot a = 1$. |
| Distributive: | $a(b + c) = ab + ac$ | |

# Two Number Tricks

Here are two number tricks. First do the trick with some specific numbers and make a conjecture about the result. Then prove the conjecture.

**1. Pick a number.**

**Multiply by 3.**

**Subtract 6.**

**Divide by 3.**

**Add 2.**

**2. Pick a number.**

**Add 4.**

**Multiply by 6.**

**Divide by 2.**

**Subtract three times the original number.**

# Direct Variation Equations of the Form $y = kx$

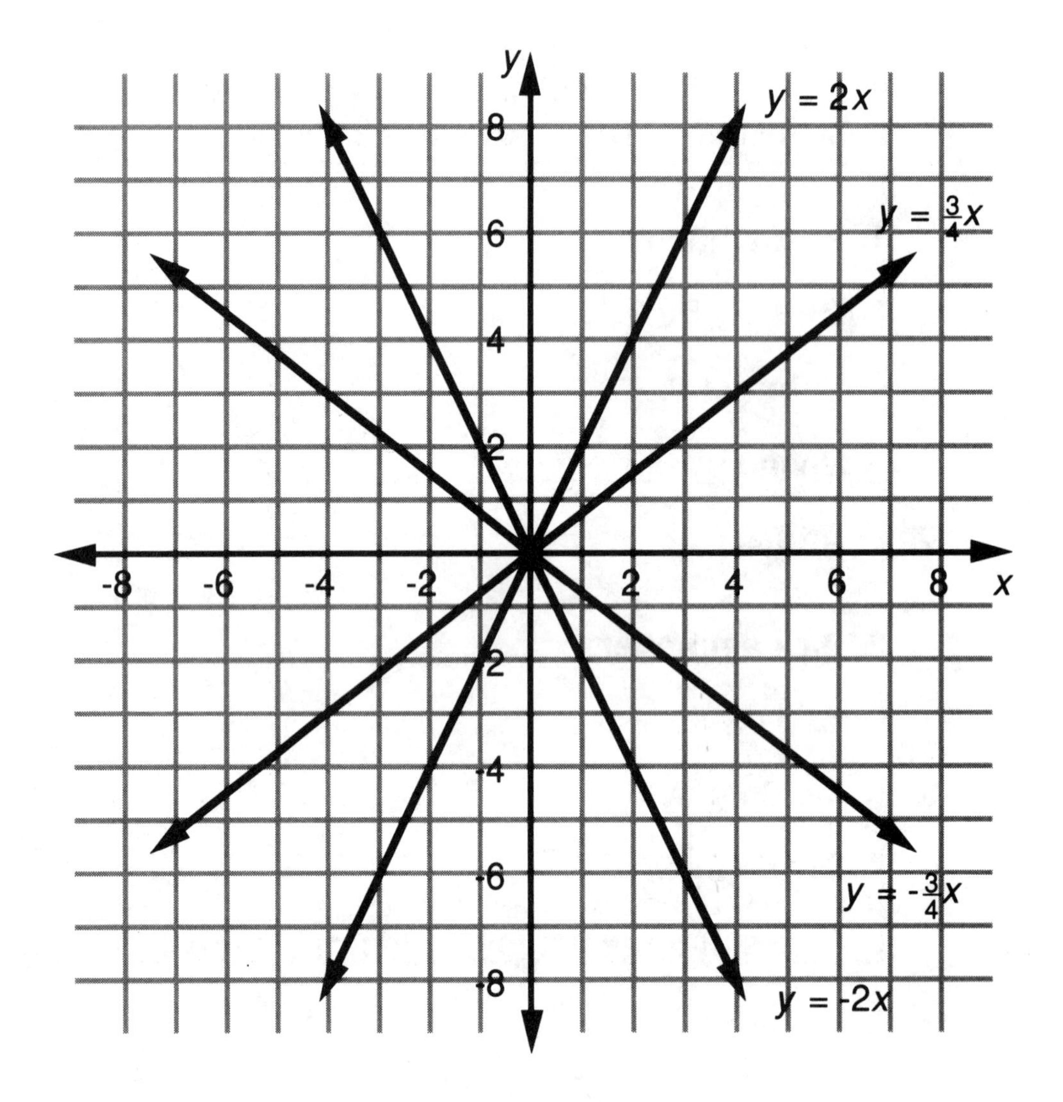

# Braking distance vs. Speed

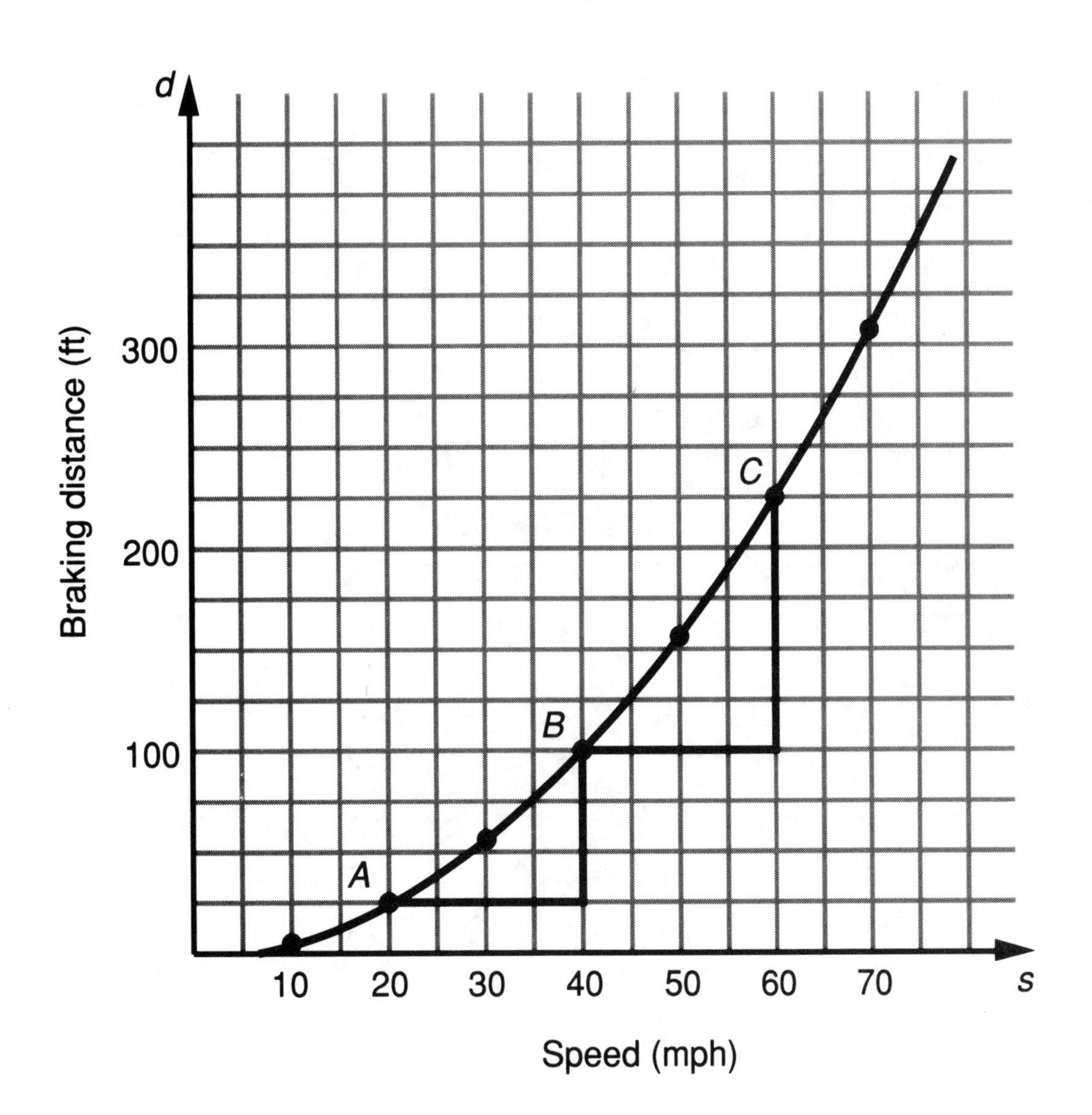

# Graphs of $y = kx^2$

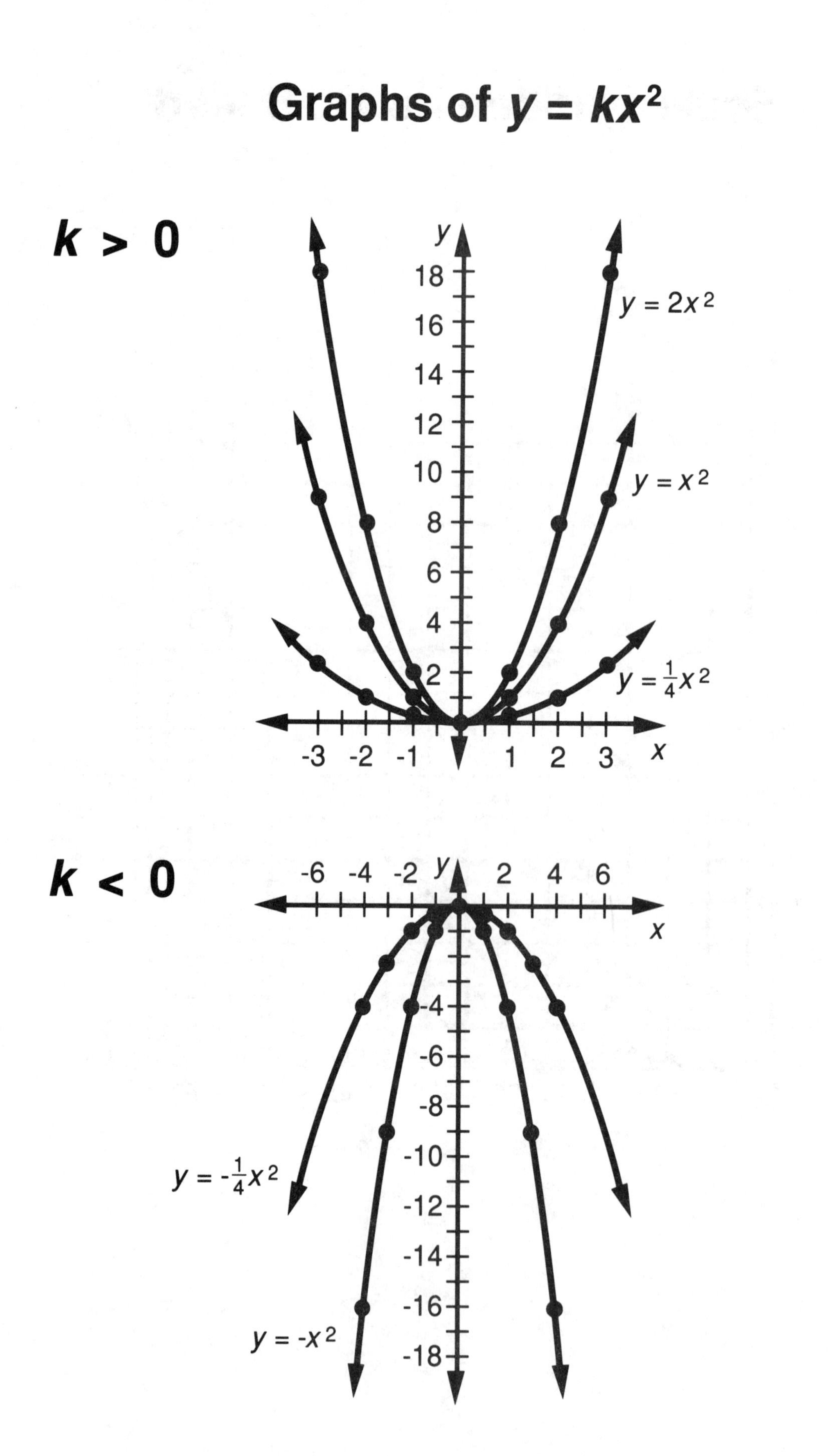

# Hours Needed to Wash Cars

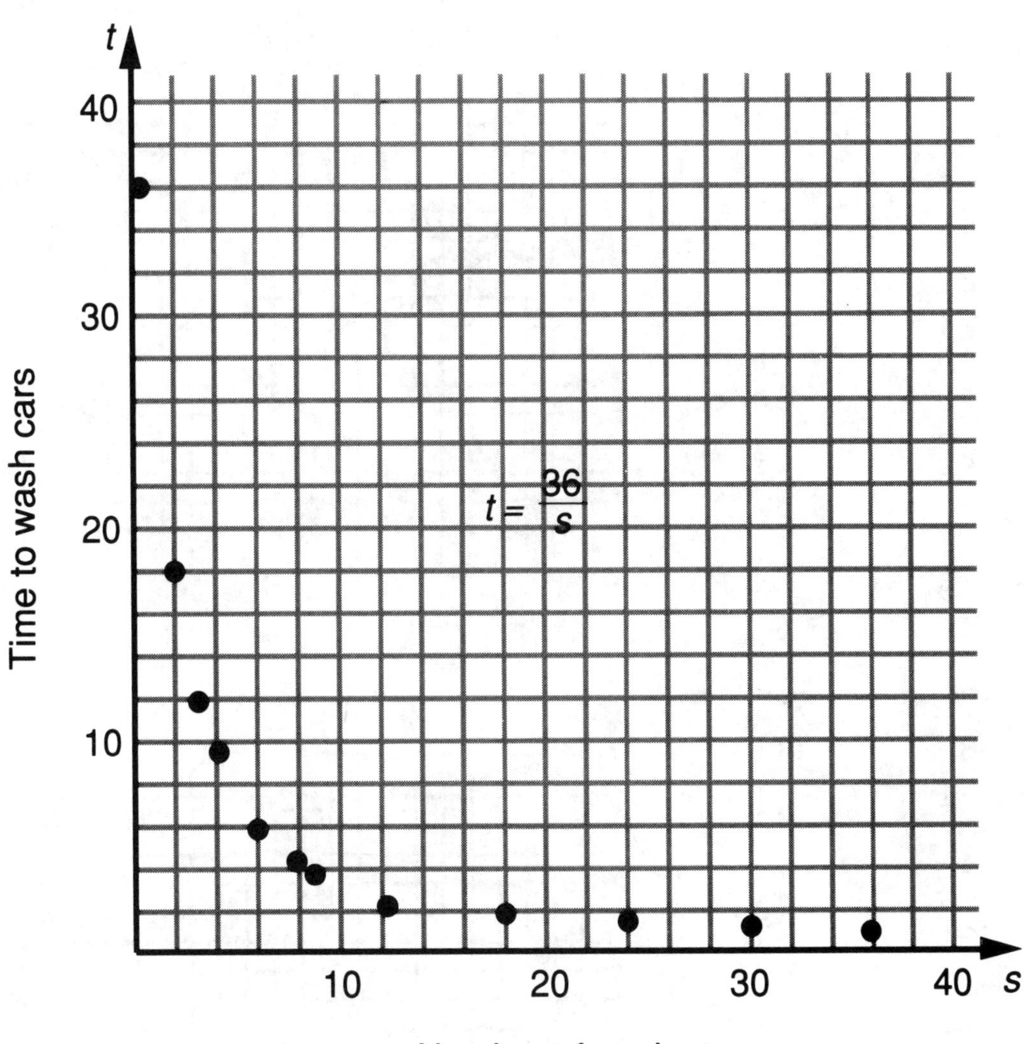

# Graphs of $y = \frac{16}{x}$ and $y = \frac{-16}{x}$

| $x$ | $y = \frac{16}{x}$ | $y = \frac{-16}{x}$ |
|---|---|---|
| 1 | 16 | -16 |
| 2 | 8 | -8 |
| 3 | $5\frac{1}{3}$ | $-5\frac{1}{3}$ |
| 4 | 4 | -4 |
| 6 | $2\frac{2}{3}$ | $-2\frac{2}{3}$ |
| 8 | 2 | -2 |
| 12 | $1\frac{1}{3}$ | $-1\frac{1}{3}$ |
| 16 | 1 | -1 |
| -1 | -16 | 16 |
| -2 | -8 | 8 |
| -3 | $-5\frac{1}{3}$ | $5\frac{1}{3}$ |
| -4 | -4 | 4 |
| -6 | $-2\frac{2}{3}$ | $2\frac{2}{3}$ |
| -8 | -2 | 2 |
| -12 | $-1\frac{1}{3}$ | $1\frac{1}{3}$ |
| -16 | -1 | 1 |

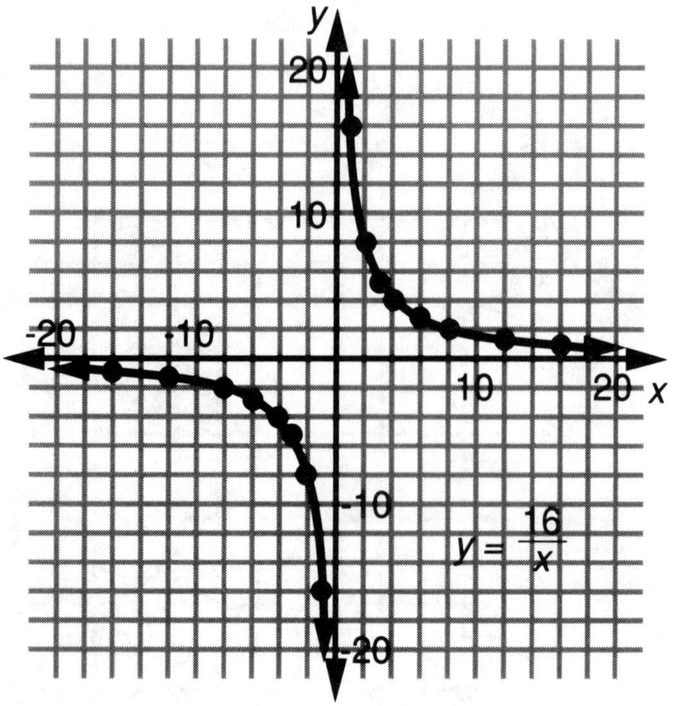

$y = \frac{16}{x}$

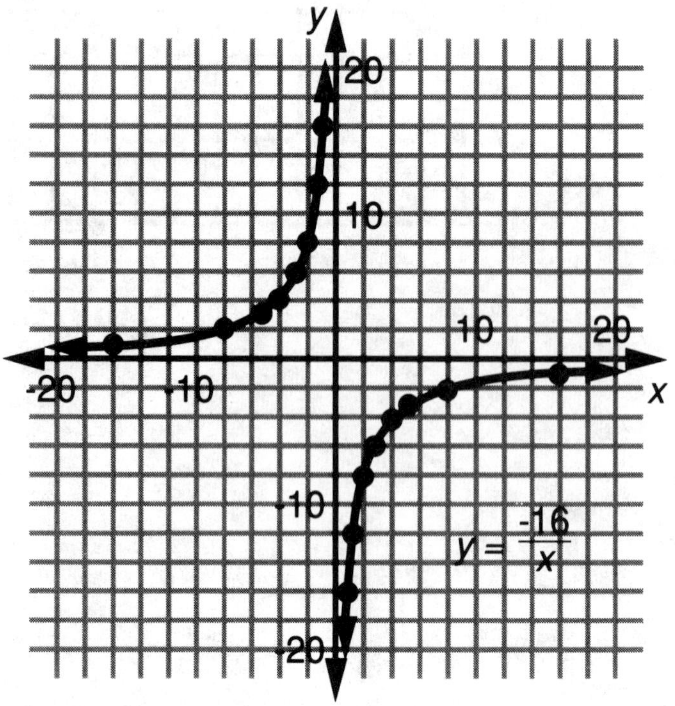

$y = \frac{-16}{x}$

# Graphs of $y = \frac{16}{x^2}$ and $y = \frac{-16}{x^2}$

| $x$ | $y = \frac{16}{x^2}$ | $y = \frac{-16}{x^2}$ |
|---|---|---|
| -8 | .25 | -.25 |
| -7 | .326531 | -.326531 |
| -6 | .444444 | -.444444 |
| -5 | .64 | -.64 |
| -4 | 1 | -1 |
| -3 | 1.77778 | -1.77778 |
| -2 | 4 | -4 |
| -1 | 16 | -16 |
| 0 | *** | *** |
| 1 | 16 | -16 |
| 2 | 4 | -4 |
| 3 | 1.77778 | -1.77778 |
| 4 | 1 | -1 |
| 5 | .64 | -.64 |
| 6 | .444444 | -.444444 |
| 7 | .326531 | -.326531 |
| 8 | .25 | -.25 |

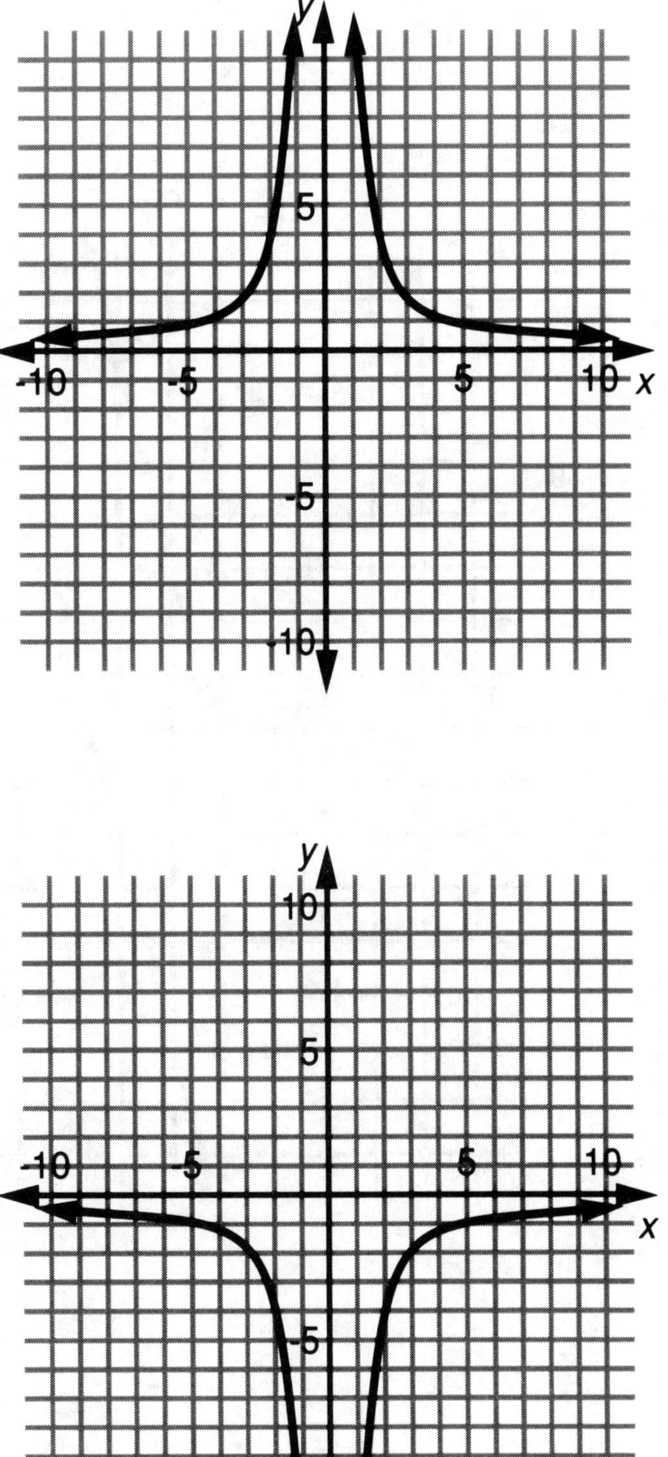

# Two Lines with the Same Slope are Parallel

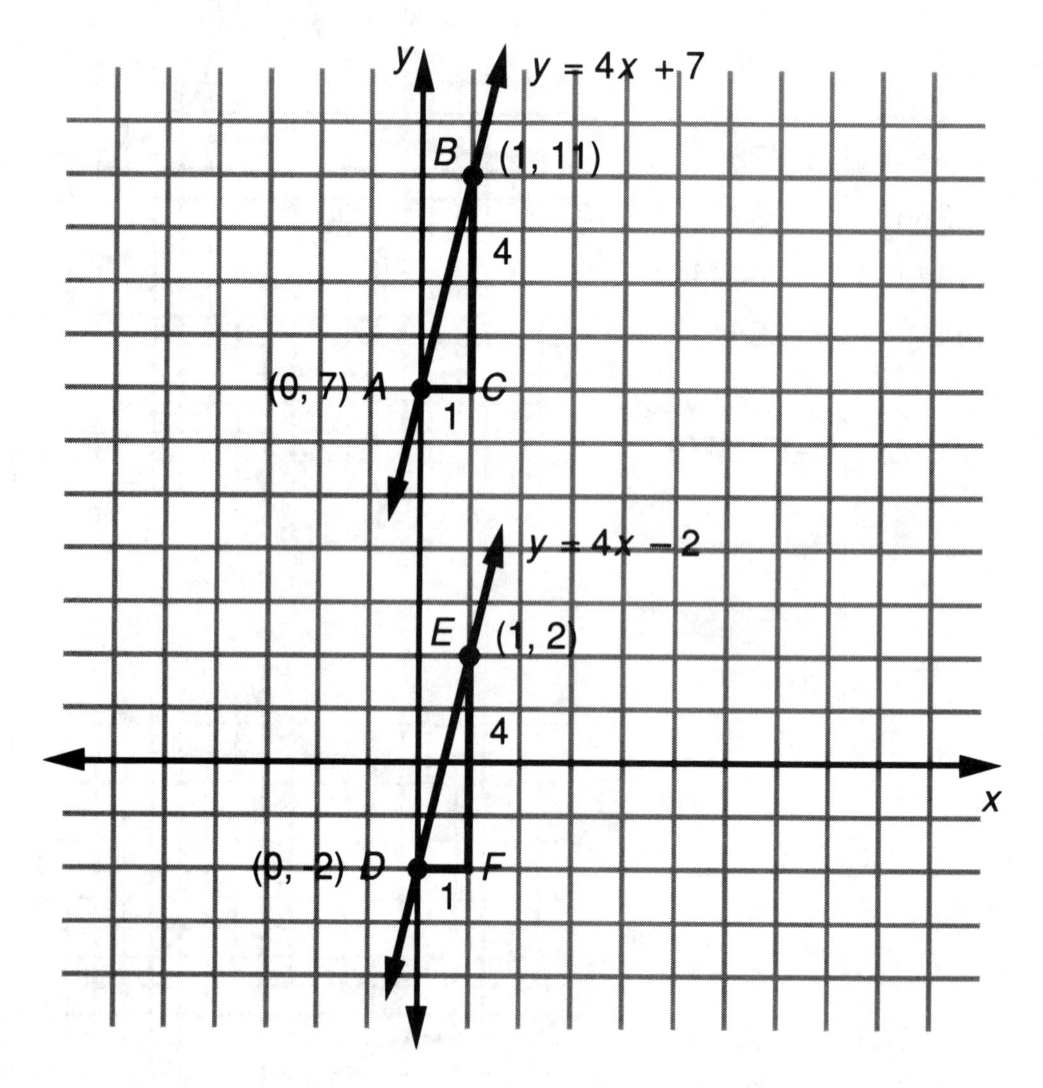

# Horace's Bicycle Trip

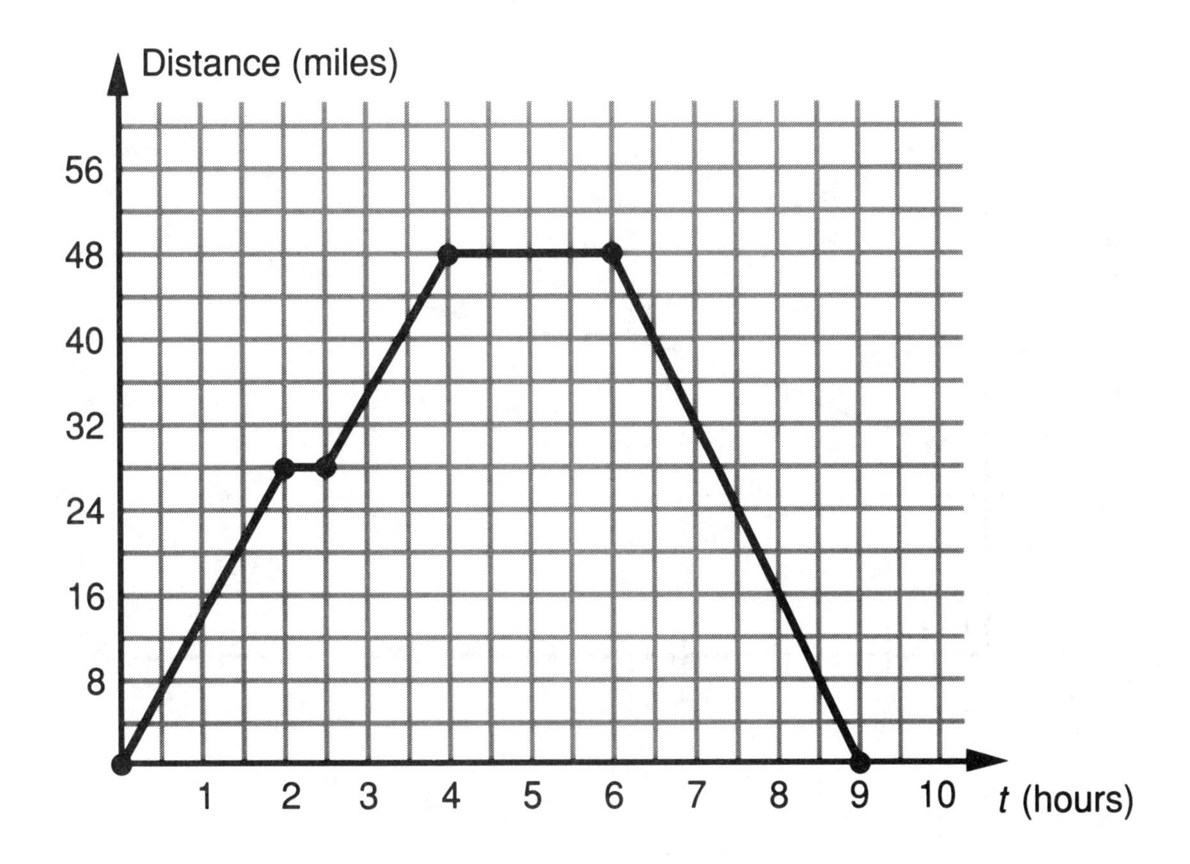

# Lesson 3-8: Additional Example

Below is a graph that describes baby Leah's weight over the first 16 weeks of her life.

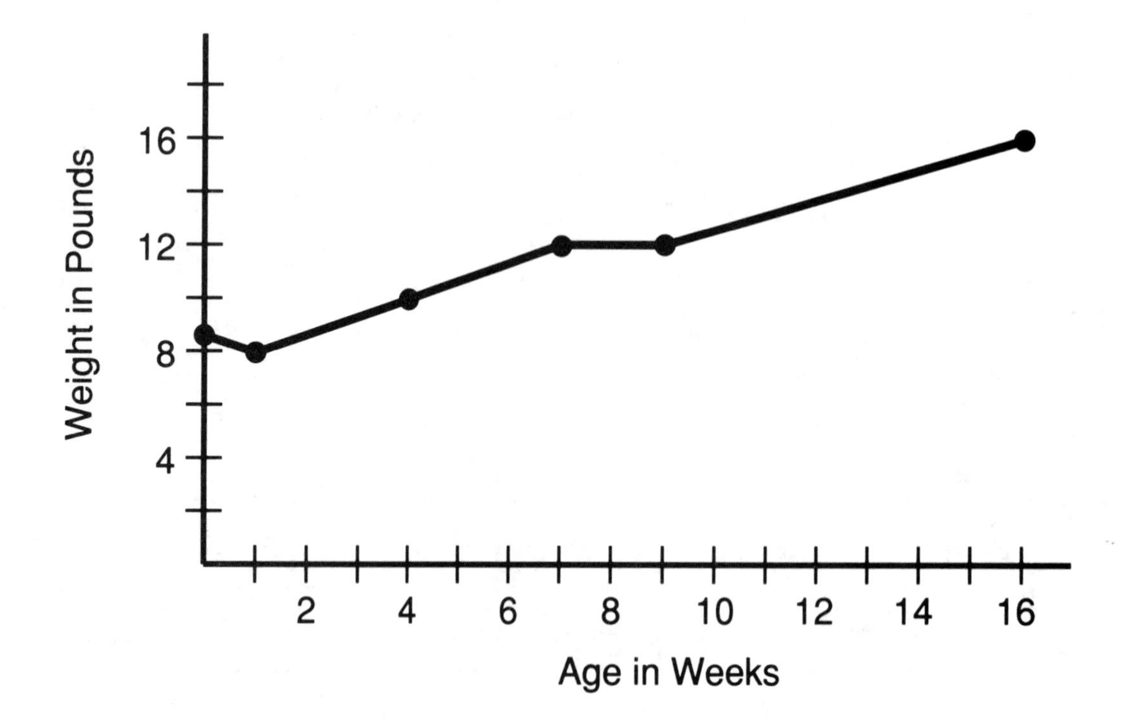


**a.** How much did the baby weigh at birth?

**b.** For how long did the baby lose weight?

**c.** What was the baby's actual weight change during weeks 2 through 7?

**d.** At what rate did the baby's weight change during weeks 2 through 7?

# Graph for Questions 9–12

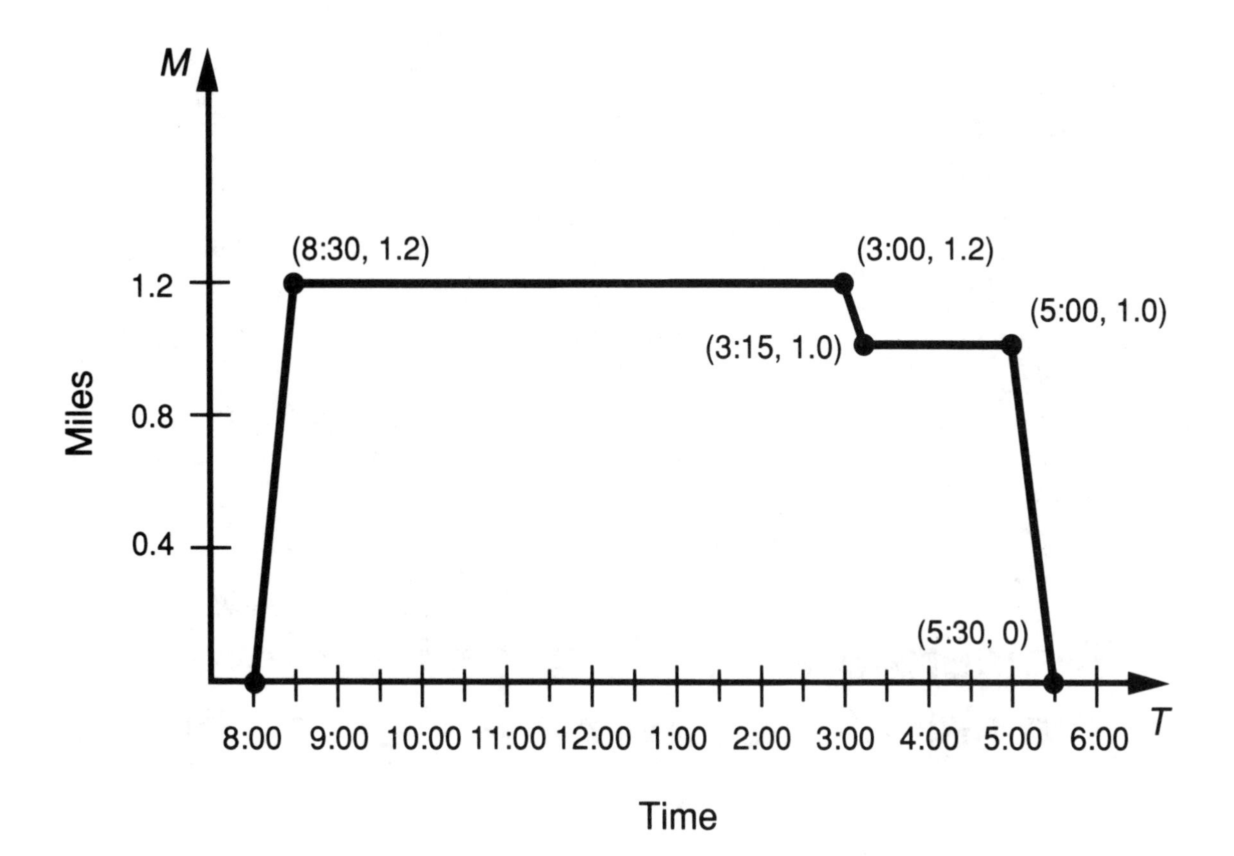

# Lesson 4-1: Additional Examples

## Medals Won in 1984 Summer Olympic Games

| | Gold | Silver | Bronze | Total |
|---|---|---|---|---|
| U.S. | 83 | 61 | 30 | 174 |
| W. Germany | 17 | 19 | 23 | 59 |
| Romania | 20 | 16 | 17 | 53 |
| Canada | 10 | 18 | 16 | 44 |
| Britain | 5 | 10 | 22 | 37 |
| China | 15 | 8 | 9 | 32 |
| Italy | 14 | 6 | 12 | 32 |
| Japan | 10 | 8 | 14 | 32 |
| France | 5 | 7 | 15 | 27 |
| all others | 47 | 66 | 84 | 197 |

## Temperatures in degrees Fahrenheit from selected cities on August 1, 1987

| | High | Low |
|---|---|---|
| Paris | 66 | 59 |
| London | 70 | 57 |
| Moscow | 75 | 57 |
| Beijing | 86 | 70 |
| Lima | 69 | 57 |
| Montreal | 76 | 53 |

# Heptagon

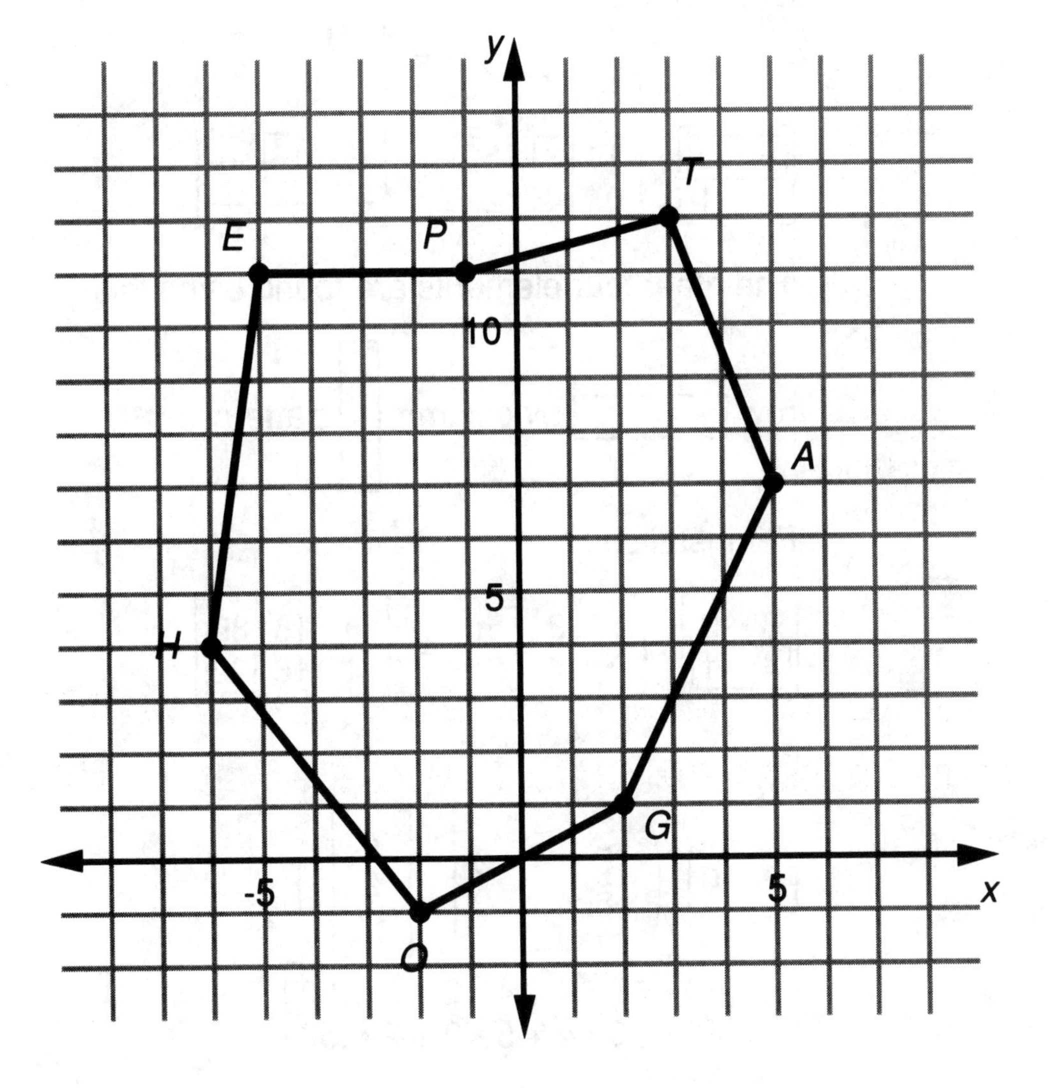

# Examples of Matrix Multiplication

**Example 1** Let $A = \underset{2 \times 2}{\begin{bmatrix} 8 & -2 \\ 4 & 1 \end{bmatrix}}$ and $B = \underset{2 \times 3}{\begin{bmatrix} 1 & 3 & 5 \\ 0 & 4 & 2 \end{bmatrix}}$. Find *AB*.

$$\begin{bmatrix} \boxed{8 \quad -2} \\ 4 \quad 1 \end{bmatrix} \begin{bmatrix} \boxed{\begin{matrix} 1 \\ 0 \end{matrix}} & \begin{matrix} 3 \\ 4 \end{matrix} & \begin{matrix} 5 \\ 2 \end{matrix} \end{bmatrix} = \begin{bmatrix} \boxed{8} & — & — \\ — & — & — \end{bmatrix}$$

$$\begin{bmatrix} \boxed{8 \quad -2} \\ 4 \quad 1 \end{bmatrix} \begin{bmatrix} \begin{matrix} 1 \\ 0 \end{matrix} & \boxed{\begin{matrix} 3 \\ 4 \end{matrix}} & \begin{matrix} 5 \\ 2 \end{matrix} \end{bmatrix} = \begin{bmatrix} 8 & \boxed{16} & — \\ — & — & — \end{bmatrix}$$

The other four elements are found using this

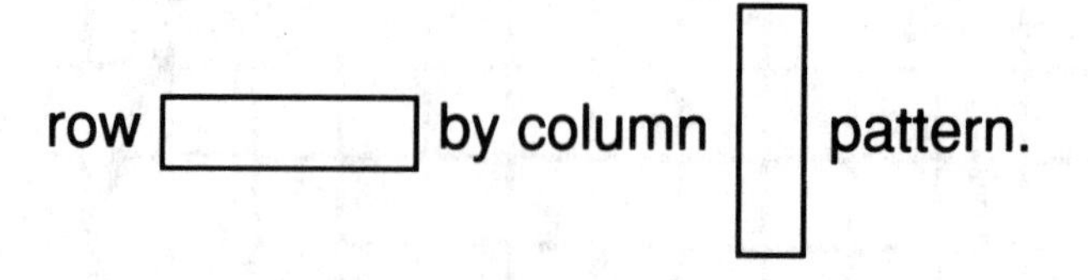


For instance:

$$\begin{bmatrix} 8 \quad -2 \\ \boxed{4 \quad 1} \end{bmatrix} \begin{bmatrix} \begin{matrix} 1 \\ 0 \end{matrix} & \begin{matrix} 3 \\ 4 \end{matrix} & \boxed{\begin{matrix} 5 \\ 2 \end{matrix}} \end{bmatrix} = \begin{bmatrix} 8 & 16 & 36 \\ 4 & 16 & \boxed{22} \end{bmatrix}$$

**Example 2**

$$\begin{bmatrix} 8 & 10 \end{bmatrix} \left( \begin{bmatrix} 5 & 4 & 3 \\ 6 & 5 & 2 \end{bmatrix} \begin{bmatrix} 4 \\ 2 \\ .50 \end{bmatrix} \right)$$

$$= \begin{bmatrix} 8 & 10 \end{bmatrix} \begin{bmatrix} 5 \cdot 4 + 4 \cdot 2 + 3 \cdot .50 \\ 6 \cdot 4 + 5 \cdot 2 + 2 \cdot .50 \end{bmatrix}$$

$$= \begin{bmatrix} 8 & 10 \end{bmatrix} \begin{bmatrix} 29.50 \\ 35 \end{bmatrix}$$

$$= \begin{bmatrix} 8 \cdot 29.50 + 10 \cdot 35 \end{bmatrix}$$

$$= \begin{bmatrix} 586 \end{bmatrix}$$

# Lesson 4-2: Questions

**4.** $\begin{bmatrix} 9 & 4 & 8 & 6 \\ 2 & 0 & 3 & 1 \\ 1 & -2 & 5 & 0 \end{bmatrix} \begin{bmatrix} 12 & 2 \\ 15 & 1 \\ 3 & 9 \\ 8 & 11 \end{bmatrix} = ?$

**5.** $\begin{bmatrix} 6 & 2 \\ 0 & 3 \end{bmatrix} \begin{bmatrix} 5 & 8 & -2 \\ -4 & 1 & 0 \end{bmatrix} = ?$

**8.** $\left( \begin{bmatrix} 8 & 10 \end{bmatrix} \begin{bmatrix} 5 & 4 & 3 \\ 6 & 5 & 2 \end{bmatrix} \right) \begin{bmatrix} 4 \\ 2 \\ .50 \end{bmatrix} = ?$

**10.** $\begin{bmatrix} 3 & 0 & 5 \\ -1 & 4 & 2 \end{bmatrix} \begin{bmatrix} 2 & -2 \\ 0 & 1 \\ -3 & 4 \end{bmatrix} = ?$

**11.** $\begin{bmatrix} 2 & -2 \\ 0 & 1 \\ 3 & 4 \end{bmatrix} \begin{bmatrix} 3 & 0 & 5 \\ -1 & 4 & 2 \end{bmatrix} = ?$

# Lesson 4-2: Questions

**13.** $\begin{bmatrix} 1 & 0 \\ 0 & 1 \end{bmatrix} \begin{bmatrix} a & b \\ c & d \end{bmatrix} = ?$ $\qquad$ $\begin{bmatrix} a & b \\ c & d \end{bmatrix} \begin{bmatrix} 1 & 0 \\ 0 & 1 \end{bmatrix} = ?$

**14.**

| | whole wheat | white | rye | English muffins |
|---|---|---|---|---|
| Shorty's | 5 | 10 | 3 | 5 |
| Slim's | 0 | 15 | 8 | 10 |

$$\begin{bmatrix} 5 & 10 & 3 & 5 \\ 0 & 15 & 8 & 10 \end{bmatrix} \begin{bmatrix} .70 \\ .70 \\ .65 \\ .80 \end{bmatrix} = ?$$

**16.** $\begin{bmatrix} 3 & 1 \\ 0 & 2 \end{bmatrix} \begin{bmatrix} x \\ 9 \end{bmatrix} = \begin{bmatrix} 10 \\ 18 \end{bmatrix}$

# Composition of Transformations

$$r_{y=x} \circ r_{y=x} (\triangle ABC)$$

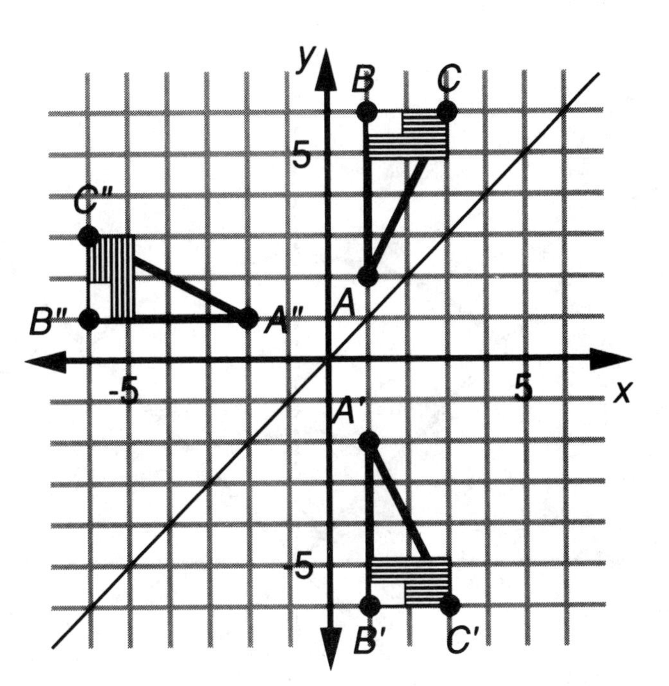


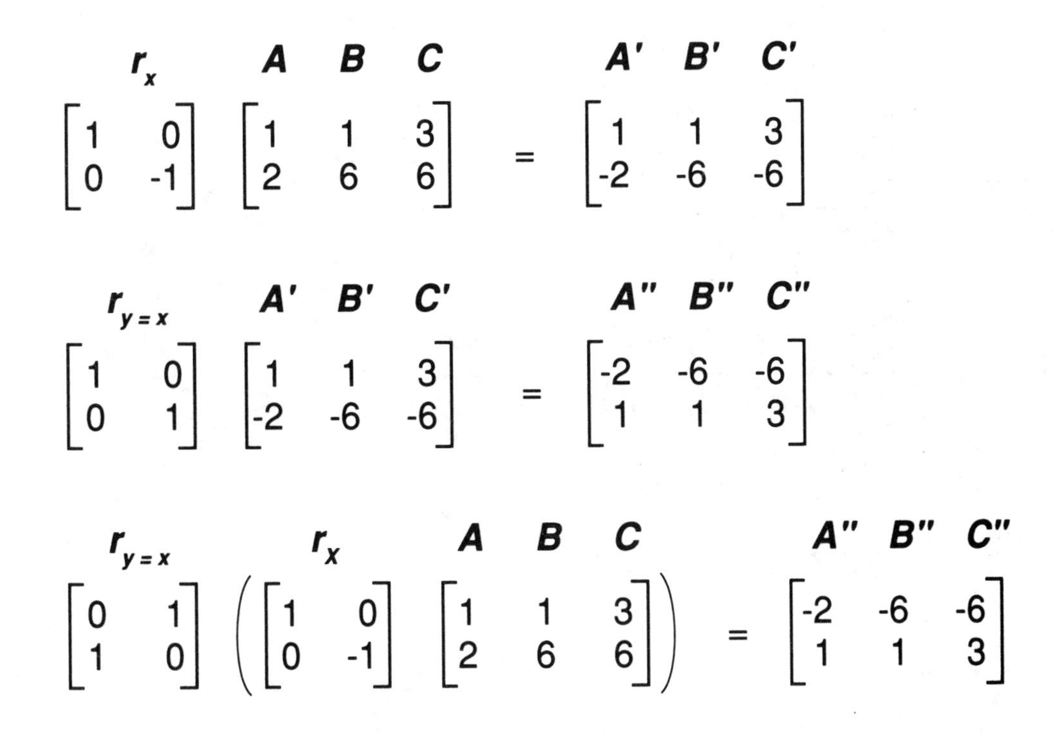

$$\underset{r_x}{\begin{bmatrix} 1 & 0 \\ 0 & -1 \end{bmatrix}} \overset{\begin{matrix} A & B & C \end{matrix}}{\begin{bmatrix} 1 & 1 & 3 \\ 2 & 6 & 6 \end{bmatrix}} = \overset{\begin{matrix} A' & B' & C' \end{matrix}}{\begin{bmatrix} 1 & 1 & 3 \\ -2 & -6 & -6 \end{bmatrix}}$$

$$\underset{r_{y=x}}{\begin{bmatrix} 1 & 0 \\ 0 & 1 \end{bmatrix}} \overset{\begin{matrix} A' & B' & C' \end{matrix}}{\begin{bmatrix} 1 & 1 & 3 \\ -2 & -6 & -6 \end{bmatrix}} = \overset{\begin{matrix} A'' & B'' & C'' \end{matrix}}{\begin{bmatrix} -2 & -6 & -6 \\ 1 & 1 & 3 \end{bmatrix}}$$

$$\underset{r_{y=x}}{\begin{bmatrix} 0 & 1 \\ 1 & 0 \end{bmatrix}} \left( \underset{r_x}{\begin{bmatrix} 1 & 0 \\ 0 & -1 \end{bmatrix}} \overset{\begin{matrix} A & B & C \end{matrix}}{\begin{bmatrix} 1 & 1 & 3 \\ 2 & 6 & 6 \end{bmatrix}} \right) = \overset{\begin{matrix} A'' & B'' & C'' \end{matrix}}{\begin{bmatrix} -2 & -6 & -6 \\ 1 & 1 & 3 \end{bmatrix}}$$

# Theorem
# If two lines with slopes $m_1$ and $m_2$ are perpendicular, then $m_1 \cdot m_2 = -1$

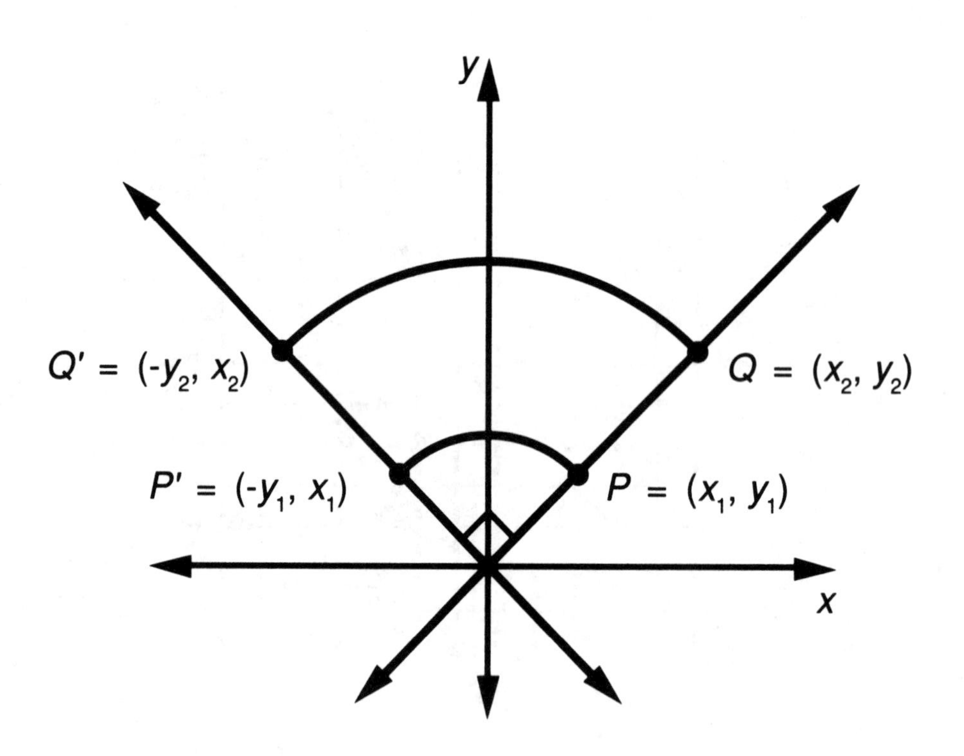


$$m_1 = \text{slope of } \overleftrightarrow{PQ} = \frac{y_2 - y_1}{x_2 - x_1}$$

$$m_2 = \text{slope of } \overleftrightarrow{P'Q'} = \frac{x_2 - x_1}{-y_2 - (-y_1)} = \frac{x_2 - x_1}{-(y_2 - y_1)} = -\frac{x_2 - x_1}{y_2 - y_1}$$

$$m_1 \cdot m_2 = \frac{y_2 - y_1}{x_2 - x_1} \cdot \left(-\frac{x_2 - x_1}{y_2 - y_1}\right)$$

$$= -1$$

# Inventory of Elizabeth's Boutique Department

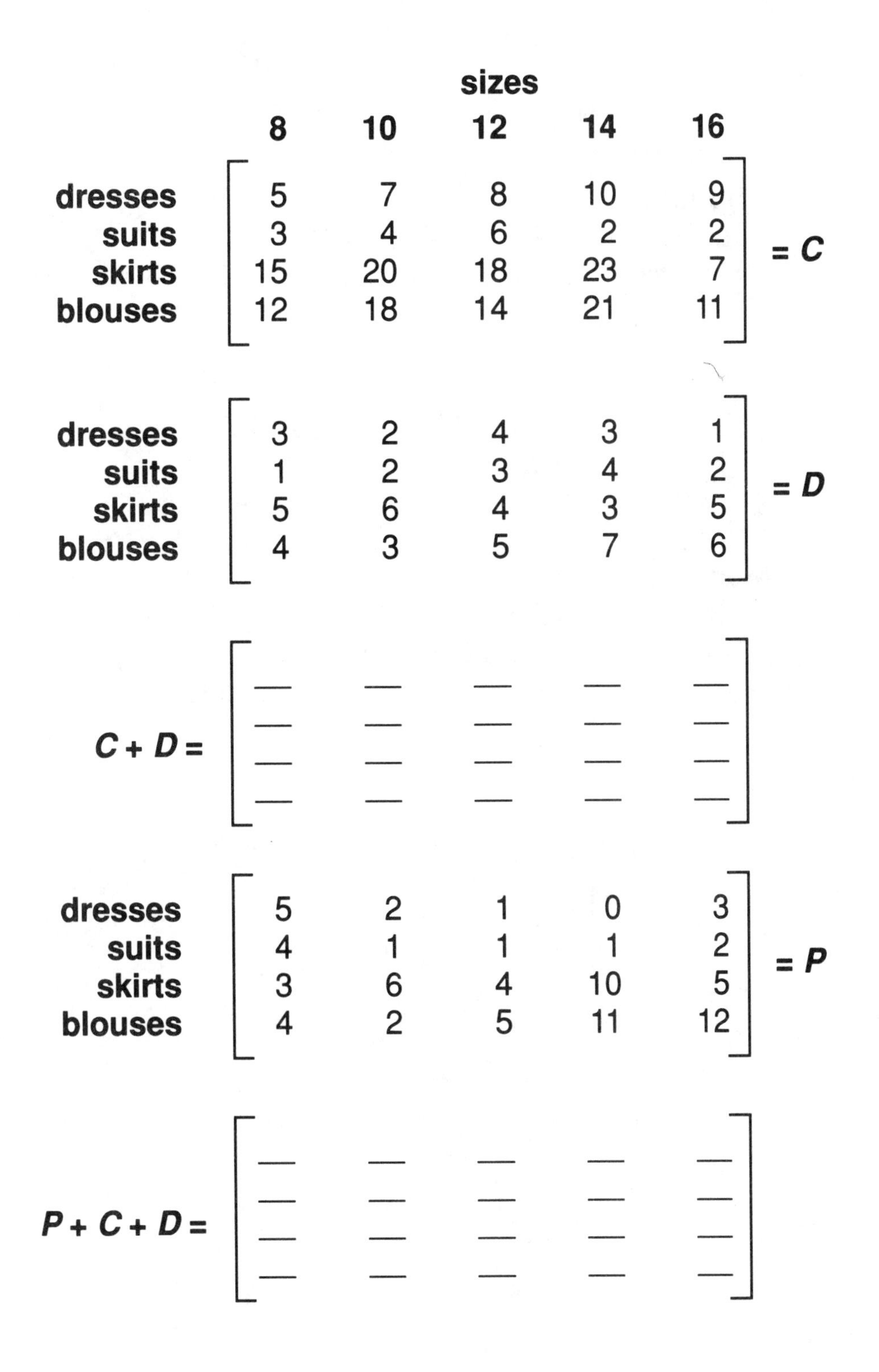

sizes

| | 8 | 10 | 12 | 14 | 16 | |
|---|---|---|---|---|---|---|
| dresses | 5 | 7 | 8 | 10 | 9 | |
| suits | 3 | 4 | 6 | 2 | 2 | = *C* |
| skirts | 15 | 20 | 18 | 23 | 7 | |
| blouses | 12 | 18 | 14 | 21 | 11 | |

| | | | | | | |
|---|---|---|---|---|---|---|
| dresses | 3 | 2 | 4 | 3 | 1 | |
| suits | 1 | 2 | 3 | 4 | 2 | = *D* |
| skirts | 5 | 6 | 4 | 3 | 5 | |
| blouses | 4 | 3 | 5 | 7 | 6 | |

$$C + D = \begin{bmatrix} \_\_ & \_\_ & \_\_ & \_\_ & \_\_ \\ \_\_ & \_\_ & \_\_ & \_\_ & \_\_ \\ \_\_ & \_\_ & \_\_ & \_\_ & \_\_ \\ \_\_ & \_\_ & \_\_ & \_\_ & \_\_ \end{bmatrix}$$

| | | | | | | |
|---|---|---|---|---|---|---|
| dresses | 5 | 2 | 1 | 0 | 3 | |
| suits | 4 | 1 | 1 | 1 | 2 | = *P* |
| skirts | 3 | 6 | 4 | 10 | 5 | |
| blouses | 4 | 2 | 5 | 11 | 12 | |

$$P + C + D = \begin{bmatrix} \_\_ & \_\_ & \_\_ & \_\_ & \_\_ \\ \_\_ & \_\_ & \_\_ & \_\_ & \_\_ \\ \_\_ & \_\_ & \_\_ & \_\_ & \_\_ \\ \_\_ & \_\_ & \_\_ & \_\_ & \_\_ \end{bmatrix}$$

# Lesson 4-9: Question 13

**1982 – 1983**

| | W | L | T | Pts. | |
|---|---|---|---|---|---|
| **Boston** | 50 | 20 | 10 | 110 | |
| **Montreal** | 42 | 24 | 14 | 98 | |
| **Buffalo** | 38 | 29 | 13 | 89 | $= A$ |
| **Quebec** | 34 | 34 | 12 | 80 | |
| **Hartford** | 19 | 54 | 7 | 45 | |

**1983 – 1984**

| | W | L | T | Pts. | |
|---|---|---|---|---|---|
| **Boston** | 49 | 25 | 6 | 104 | |
| **Montreal** | 35 | 40 | 5 | 75 | |
| **Buffalo** | 48 | 25 | 7 | 103 | $= B$ |
| **Quebec** | 42 | 28 | 10 | 94 | |
| **Hartford** | 28 | 42 | 10 | 66 | |

| | W | L | T | Pts. |
|---|---|---|---|---|
| | ___ | ___ | ___ | ___ |
| | ___ | ___ | ___ | ___ |
| $B - A = M =$ | ___ | ___ | ___ | ___ |
| | ___ | ___ | ___ | ___ |
| | ___ | ___ | ___ | ___ |

# Transformations and Their Matrices

## Transformations Yielding Images Congruent to Preimages

Reflections:

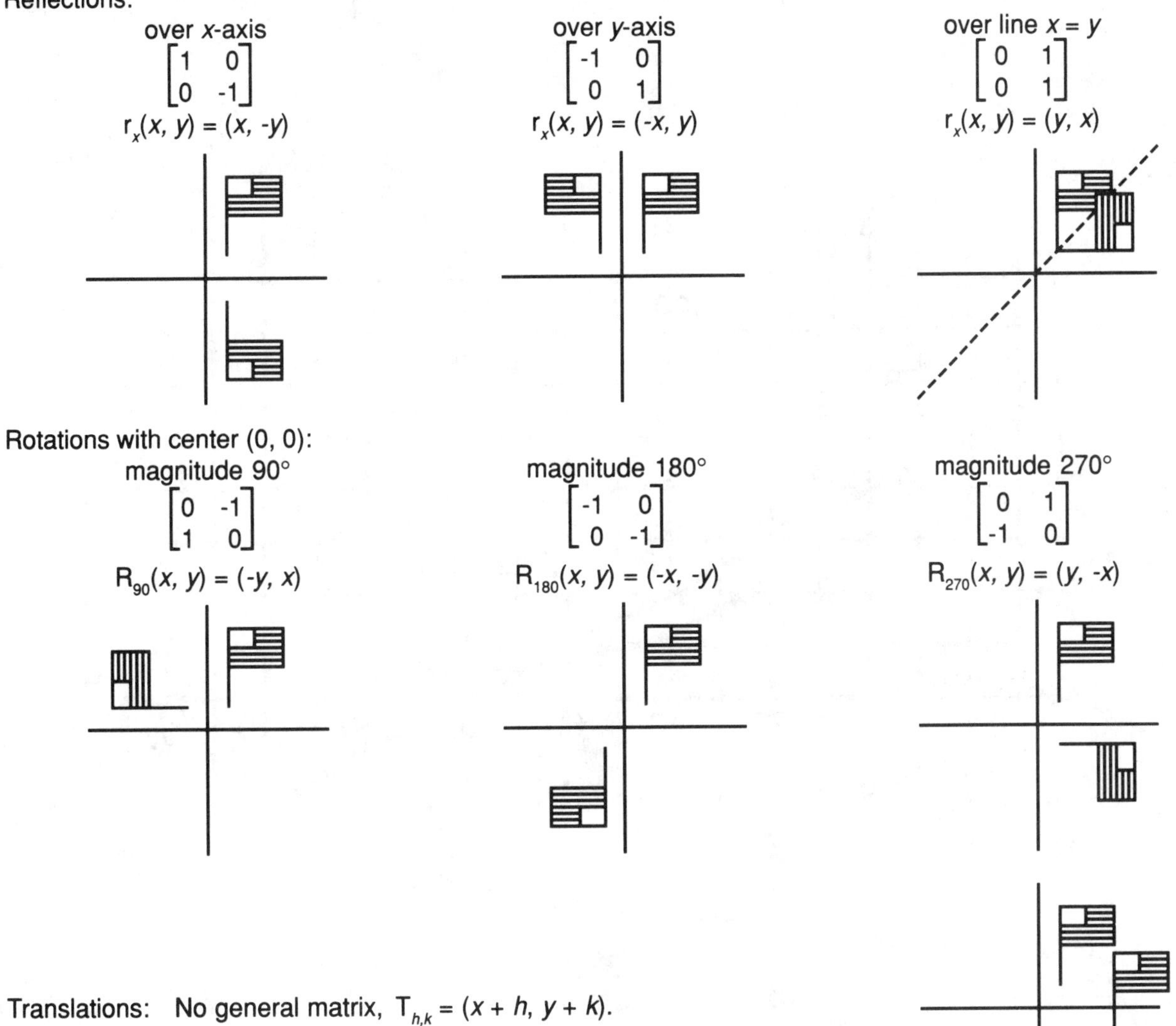

over $x$-axis

$$\begin{bmatrix} 1 & 0 \\ 0 & -1 \end{bmatrix}$$

$r_x(x, y) = (x, -y)$

over $y$-axis

$$\begin{bmatrix} -1 & 0 \\ 0 & 1 \end{bmatrix}$$

$r_x(x, y) = (-x, y)$

over line $x = y$

$$\begin{bmatrix} 0 & 1 \\ 0 & 1 \end{bmatrix}$$

$r_x(x, y) = (y, x)$

Rotations with center (0, 0):

magnitude 90°

$$\begin{bmatrix} 0 & -1 \\ 1 & 0 \end{bmatrix}$$

$R_{90}(x, y) = (-y, x)$

magnitude 180°

$$\begin{bmatrix} -1 & 0 \\ 0 & -1 \end{bmatrix}$$

$R_{180}(x, y) = (-x, -y)$

magnitude 270°

$$\begin{bmatrix} 0 & 1 \\ -1 & 0 \end{bmatrix}$$

$R_{270}(x, y) = (y, -x)$

Translations: No general matrix, $T_{h,k} = (x + h, y + k)$.

## Transformations Yielding Images Similar to Preimages

Size changes with center (0, 0), magnitude $k$:

$$\begin{bmatrix} k & 0 \\ 0 & k \end{bmatrix}$$

$S_k(x, y) = (kx, ky)$

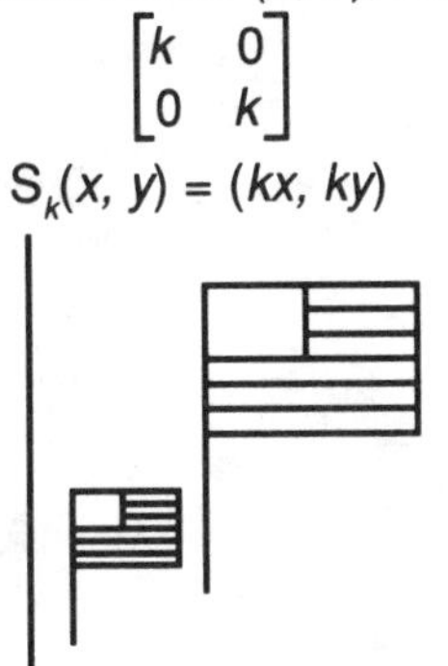

## Other Transformations

Scale changes with horizontal magnitude $a$ and vertical magnitude $b$:

$$\begin{bmatrix} a & 0 \\ 0 & b \end{bmatrix}$$

$S_{a,b}(x, y) = (ax, by)$

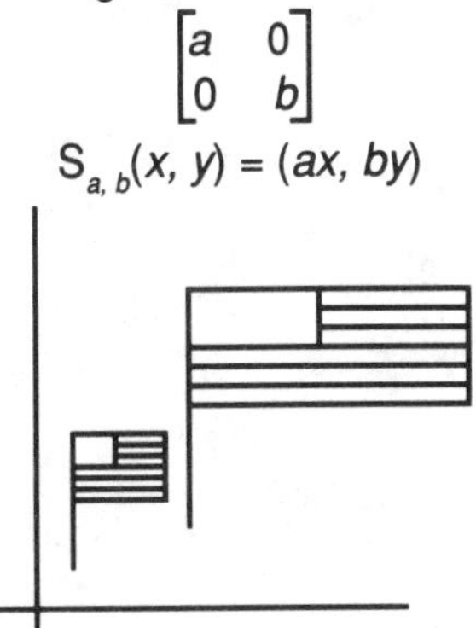

# Lesson 5-2: Example 2

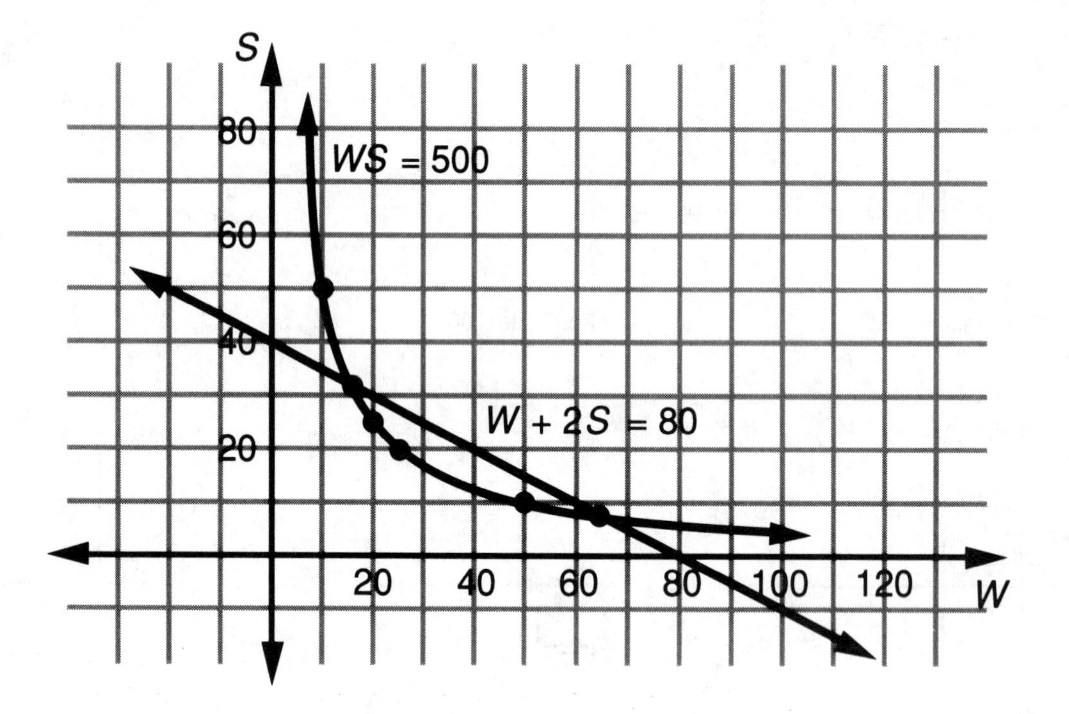

# Lesson 5-7: Example 2

| | Chairs | Desks | Total Hours Available |
|---|---|---|---|
| **Hours of carpentry per piece** | 4 | 8 | 8000 |
| **Hours of finishing per piece** | 2 | 1 | 1300 |

Let $x$ = number of chairs to be made per week

$y$ = number of desks to be made per week

$$\begin{cases} x \geq 0 \\ y \geq 0 \\ 4x + 8y \leq 8000 \\ 2x + y \leq 1300 \end{cases}$$

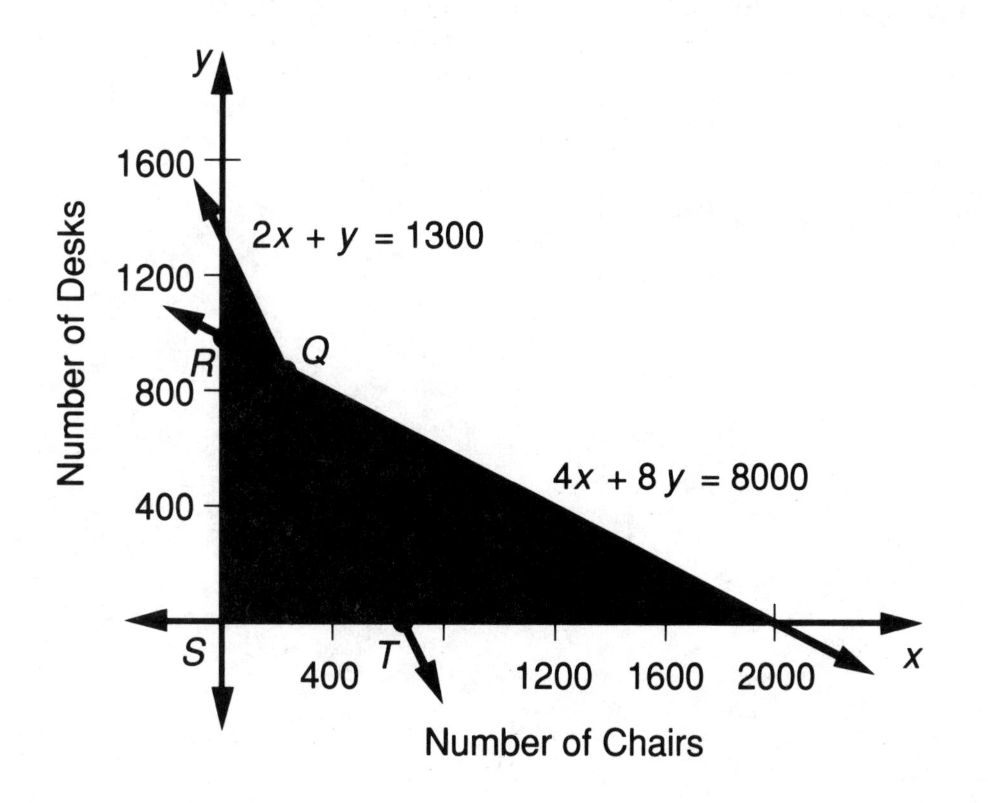

# Lesson 5-7: Additional Example

The Random Company manufactures two products, Zeta and Beta. Each product must pass through two processing operations. Zeta takes one hour each on processes number one and two. Beta takes 2 hours on process one and 3 hours on process two. Process one has a total capacity of 1000 hours per day, process two, 1275 hours per day.

a. Make a table to illustrate the information.
b. Identify the variables.
c. Write sentences to model each step in the process.
d. Graph the solution to the system.
e. Identify the vertices of the feasible region.

# Lesson 5-7: Question 14

A clothier makes women's suits and coats from nylon and wool. Each suit requires 2 yards of nylon lining and 3 yards of wool. Each coat requires 3 yards of nylon lining and 4 yards of wool. Only 42 yards of nylon lining and 58 yards of wool are in stock.

Let $s$ = the number of suits

$c$ = the number of coats

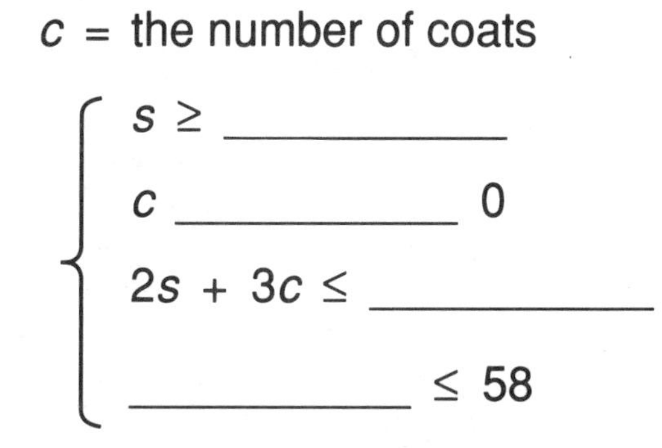

$$\begin{cases} s \geq \underline{\hspace{3cm}} \\ c \ \underline{\hspace{3cm}} \ 0 \\ 2s + 3c \leq \underline{\hspace{3cm}} \\ \underline{\hspace{3cm}} \leq 58 \end{cases}$$

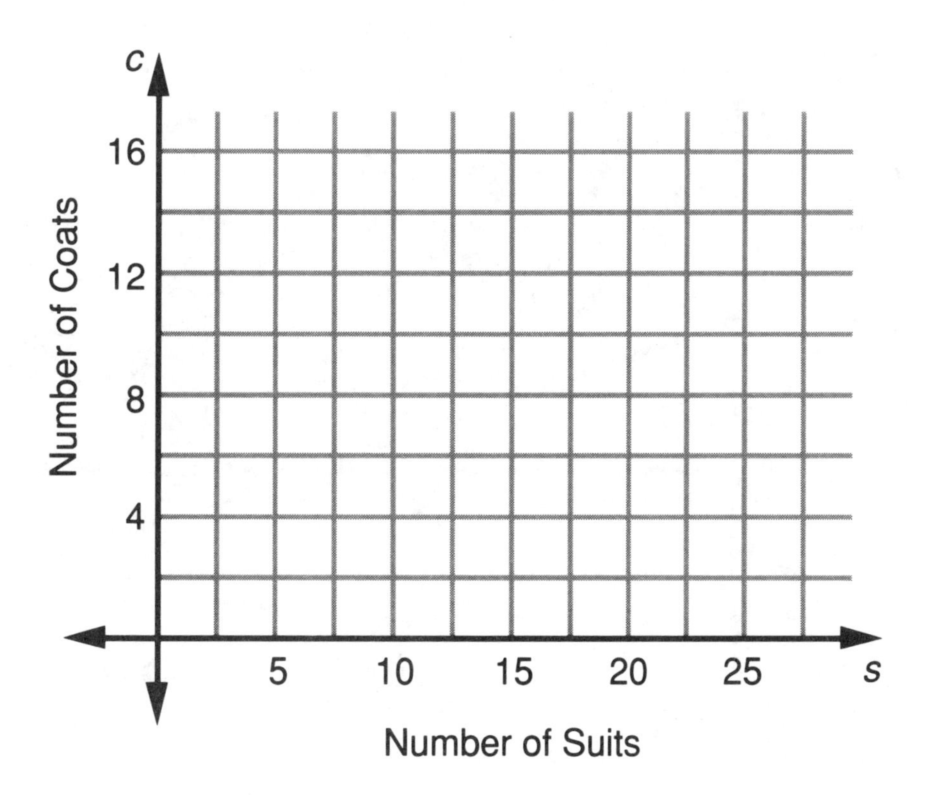

# Lesson 5-8: Example

$$\begin{cases} f \geq 0 \\ e \geq 0 \\ 100f + 310e \geq 1000 \\ 151e \geq 200 \\ 1.2f + e \geq 6 \\ 122f + 70e \geq 600 \end{cases}$$

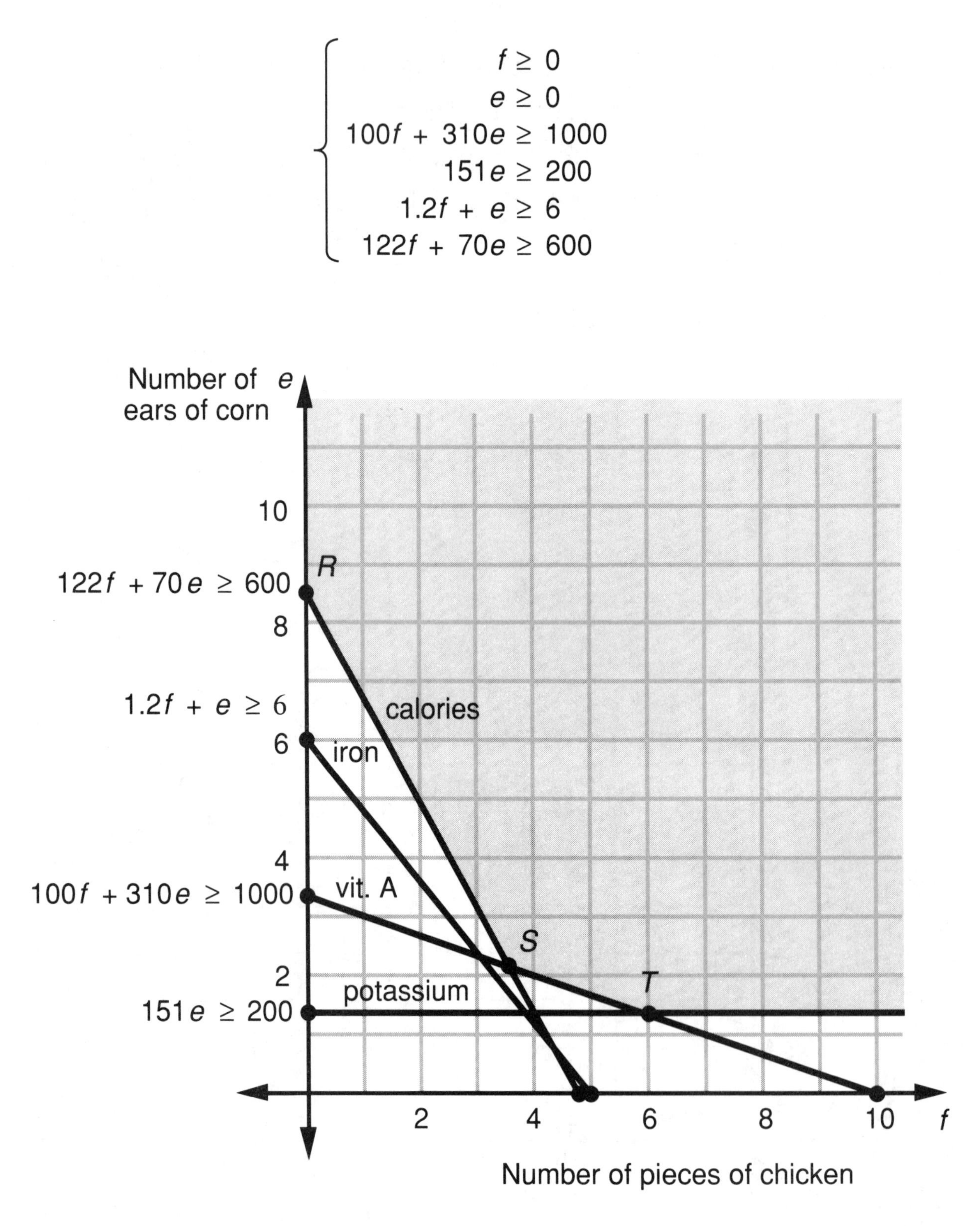

# Lesson 5-8: Additional Example

Use linear programming to solve the following problem.

Jeano's candy factory packages bags of mixed nuts. Jeano has 75 pounds of cashews and 120 pounds of peanuts. They are to be mixed in 1-pound packages in the following way: a lower-grade package that contains 4 ounces of cashews and 12 ounces of peanuts and a higher grade mixture that contains 8 ounces of cashews and 8 ounces of peanuts. A profit of $0.35 per package will be made on the low-grade mixture, and a profit of $0.55 per package will be made on the high-grade mixture. How many packages of each mixture should Jeano make to obtain the maximum profit?

(Hint: Use 75 lb = 1200 oz)

# Lesson 5-9: Example

| | Metal Used | Time to Make |
|---|---|---|
| **for each necklace** | 50 g | 30 min |
| **for each bracelet** | 200 g | 20 min |
| **Total available** | 10,000 g | 20 hours |

$$\begin{cases} x \geq 0 \\ y \geq 0 \\ 50x + 200y \leq 10{,}000 \\ 30x + 20y \leq 1{,}200 \end{cases}$$

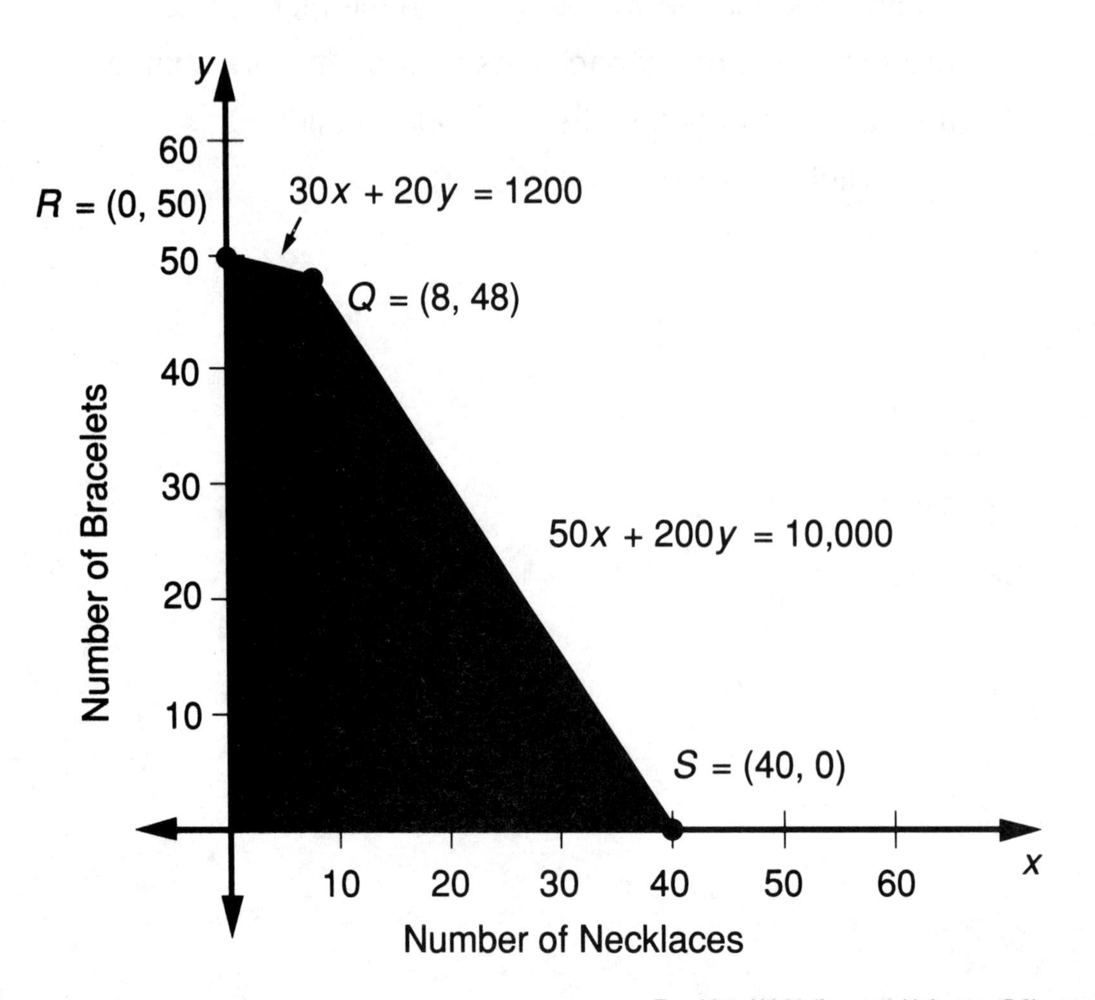

# Lesson 6-2: Example 1

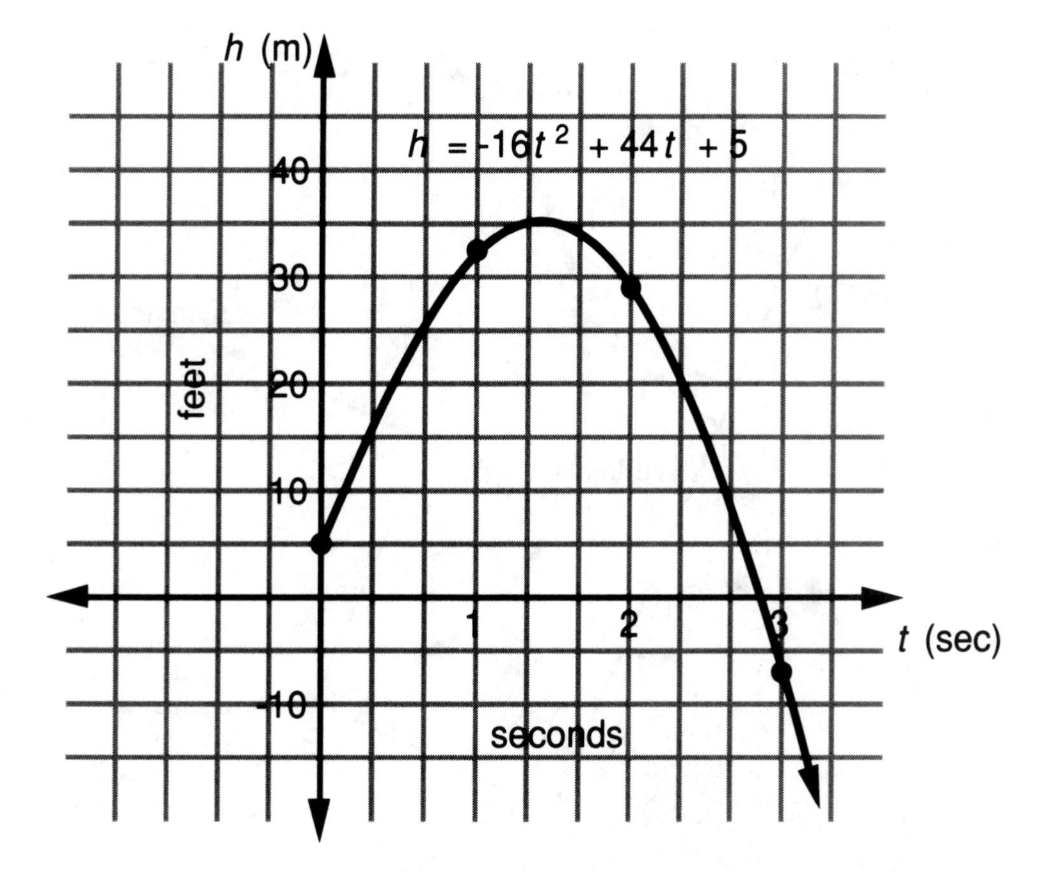

# A Parabola is Determined by a Focus and Directrix

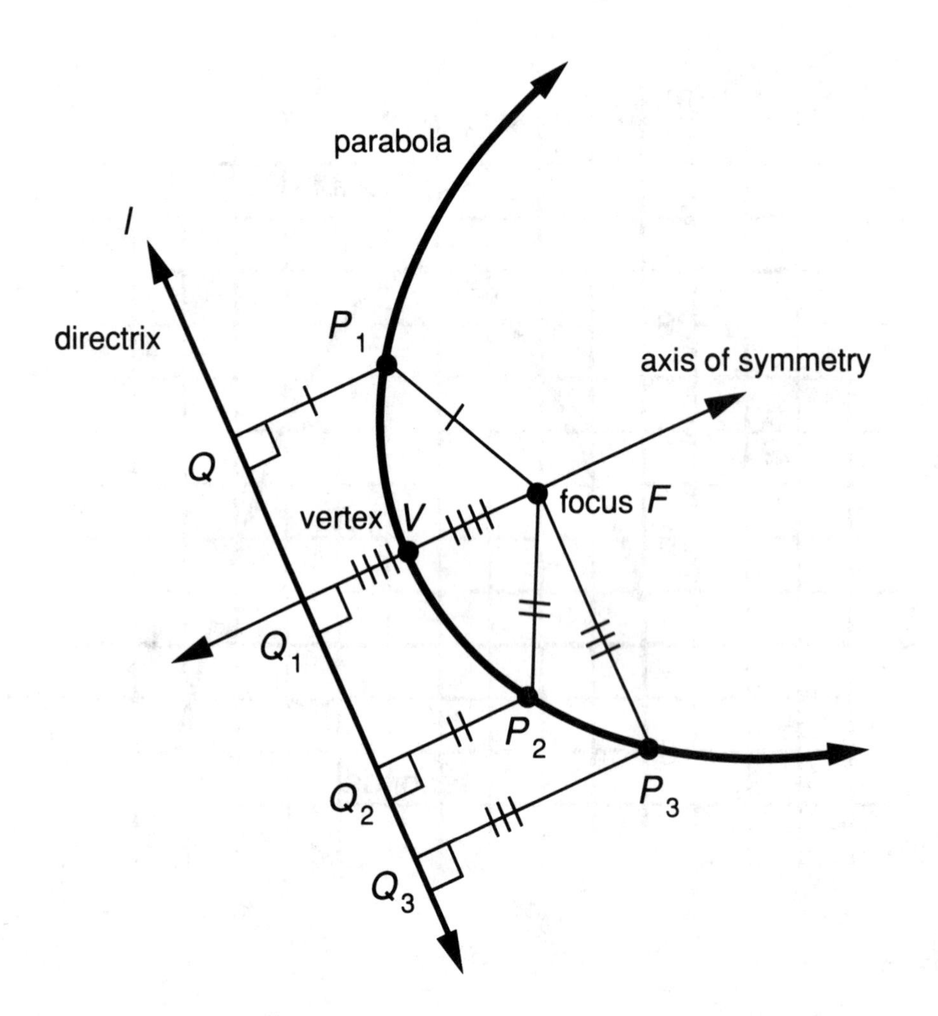

# Lesson 6-4: Example 1

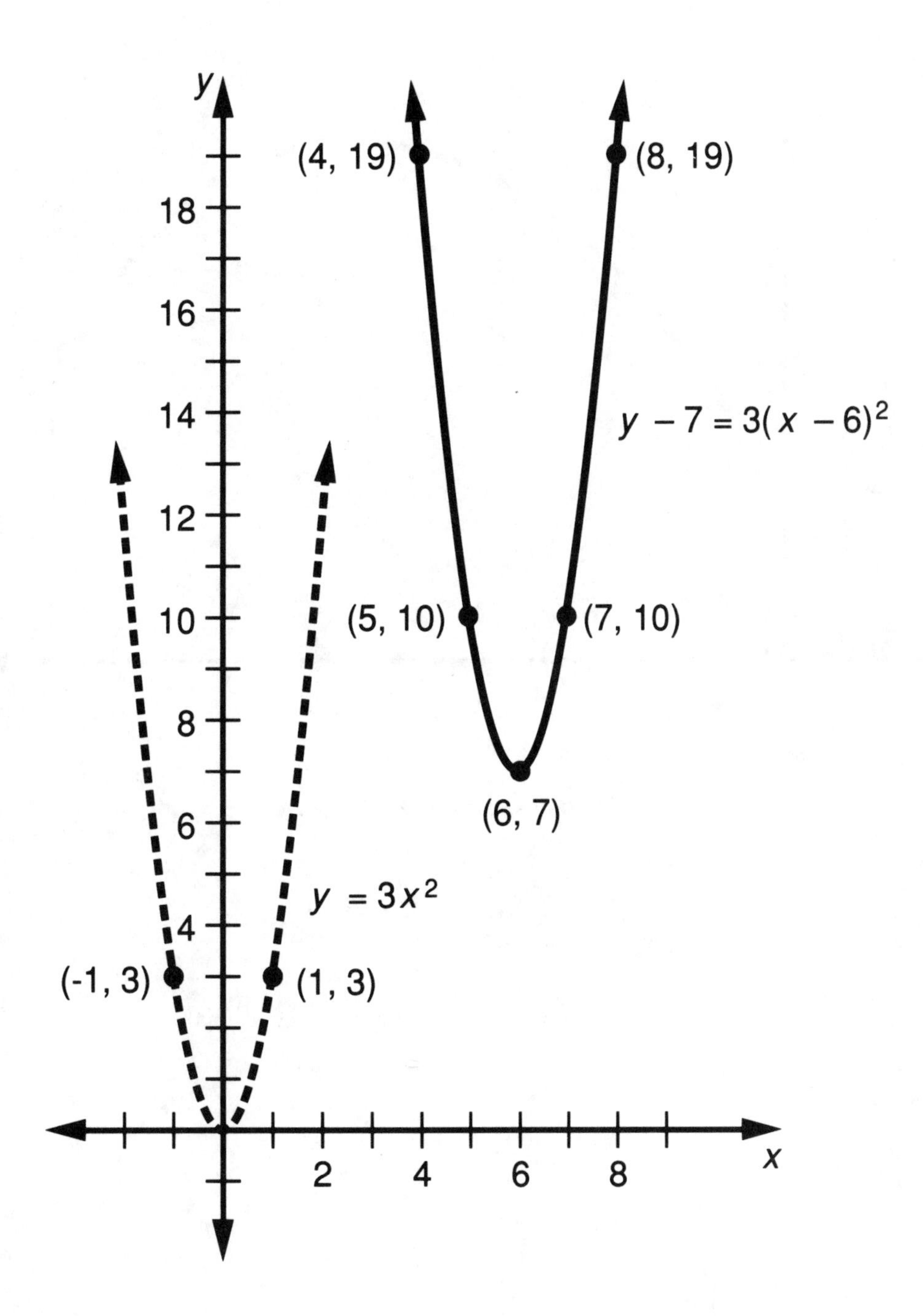

# Path of a Batted Ball

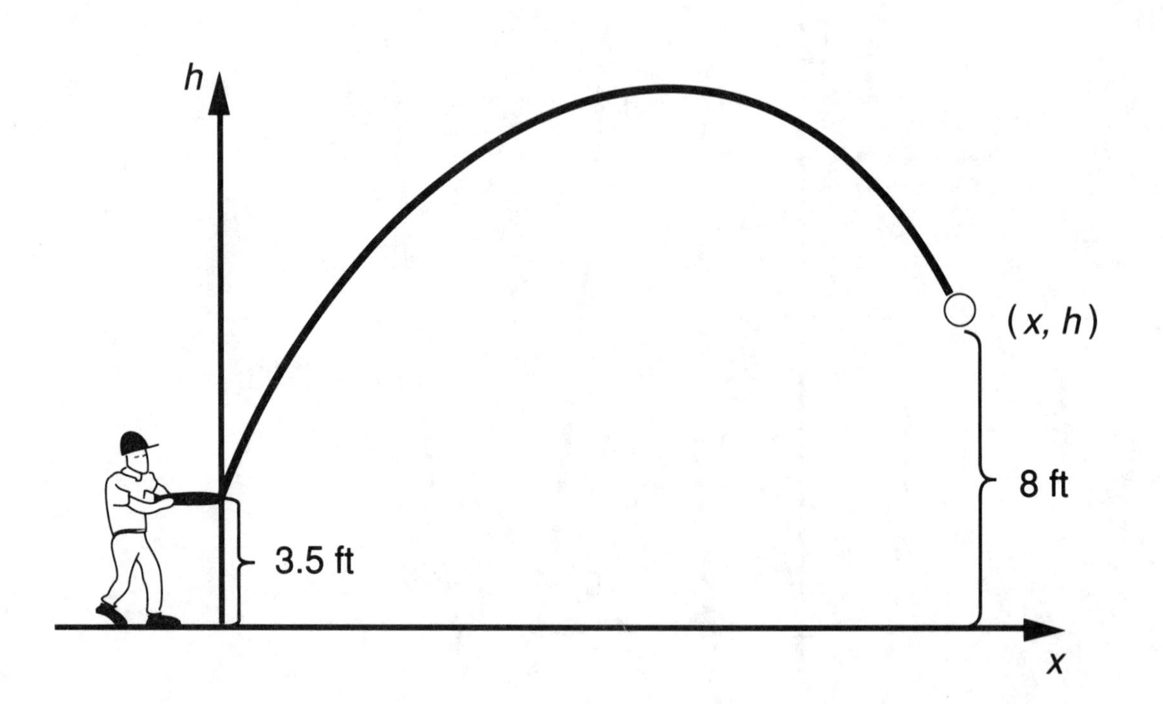


$$h = -.005x^2 + 2x + 3.5$$

# Proof of the Quadratic Formula

If $ax^2 + bx + c = 0$ and $a \neq 0$, then $x = \dfrac{-b \pm \sqrt{b^2 - 4ac}}{2a}$.

Proof

$$x^2 + \frac{b}{a}x + \frac{c}{a} = 0$$

$$x^2 + \frac{b}{a}x = -\frac{c}{a}$$

$$x^2 + \frac{b}{a}x + \frac{b^2}{4a^2} = \frac{b^2}{4a^2} - \frac{c}{a}$$

$$\left(x + \frac{b}{2a}\right)^2 = \frac{b^2}{4a^2} - \frac{c}{a}$$

$$\left(x + \frac{b}{2a}\right)^2 = \frac{b^2}{4a^2} - \frac{4ac}{4a^2}$$

$$\left(x + \frac{b}{2a}\right)^2 = \frac{b^2 - 4ac}{4a^2}$$

$$x + \frac{b}{2a} = \frac{\pm\sqrt{b^2 - 4ac}}{2a}$$

$$x = \frac{-b \pm \sqrt{b^2 - 4ac}}{2a}$$

# Complex Number System

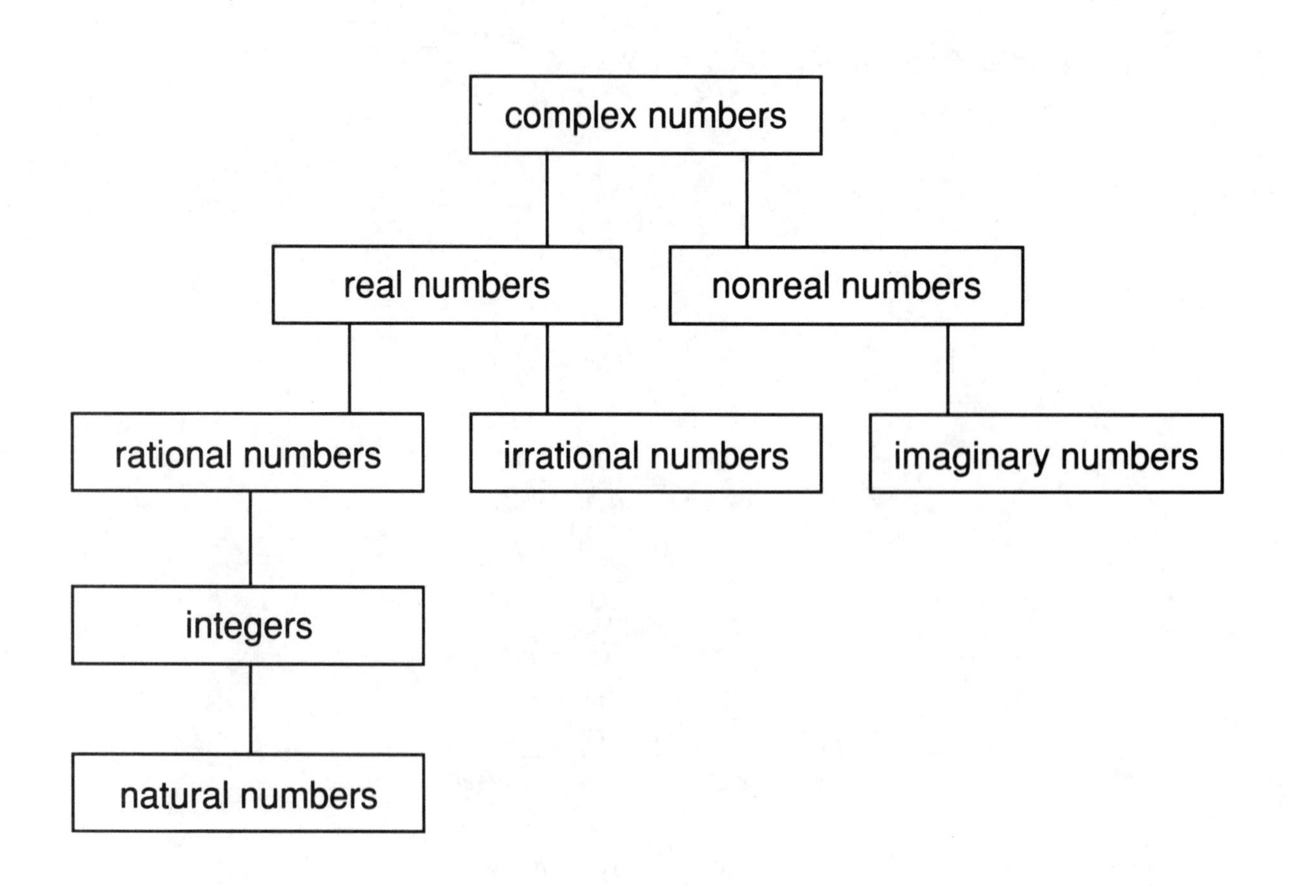

# Graph of a Parabola

$$y - k = a(x - h)^2$$

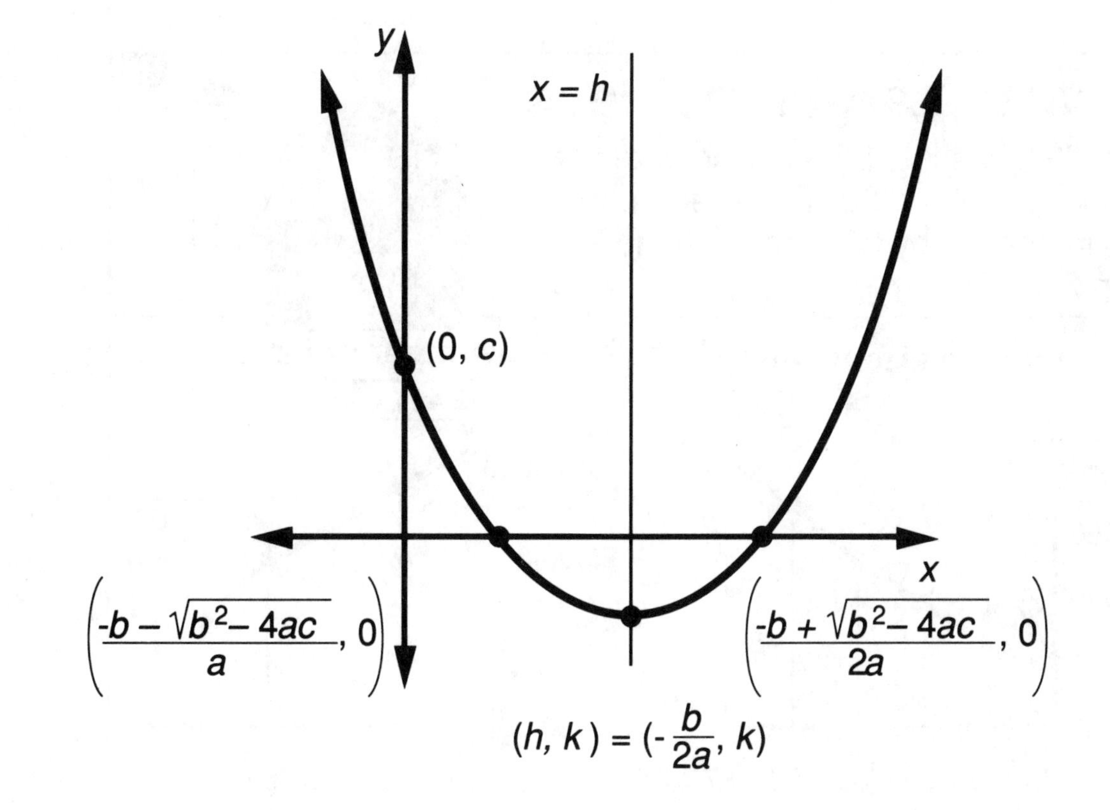

# Lesson 7-1: Questions 16–18

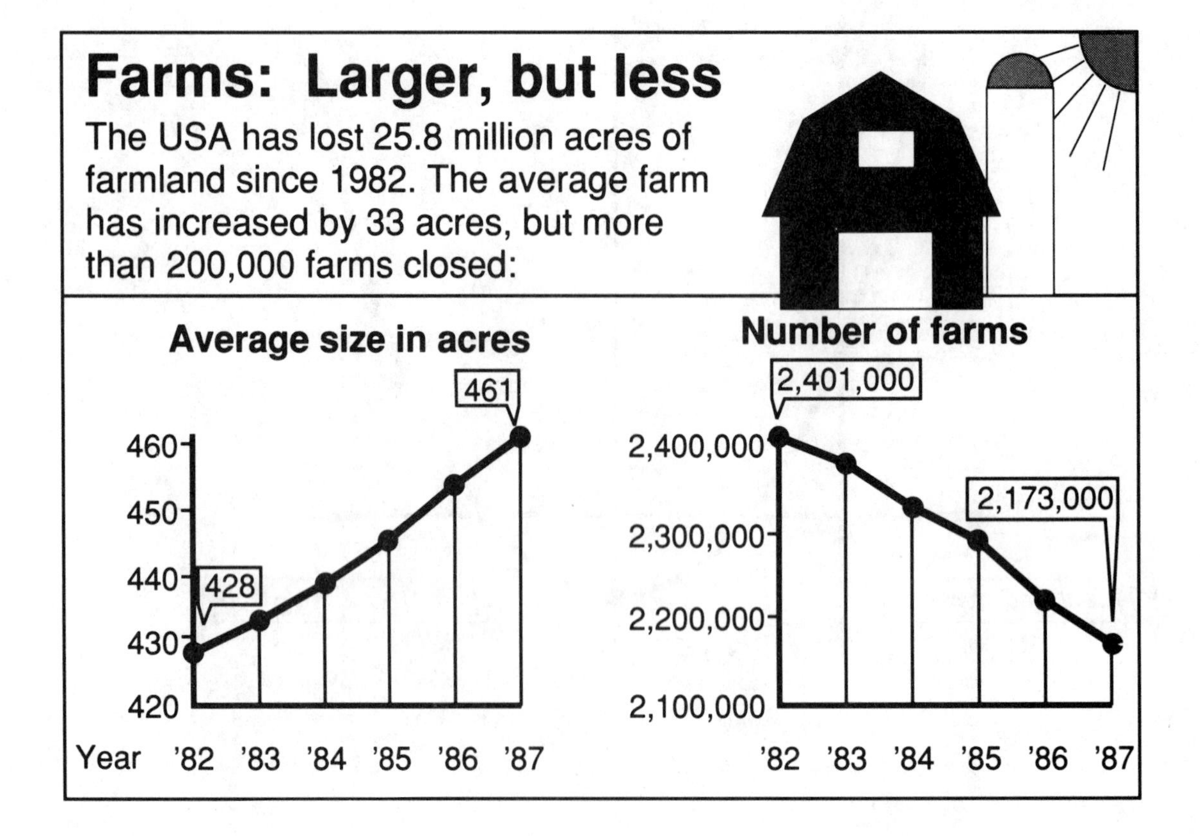
Farms: Larger, but less
The USA has lost 25.8 million acres of farmland since 1982. The average farm has increased by 33 acres, but more than 200,000 farms closed:
Average size in acres
461
460
450
440
428
430
420
Year '82 '83 '84 '85 '86 '87
Number of farms
2,401,000
2,400,000
2,173,000
2,300,000
2,200,000
2,100,000
'82 '83 '84 '85 '86 '87

# Graphs of Three Functions Related to Braking Distance

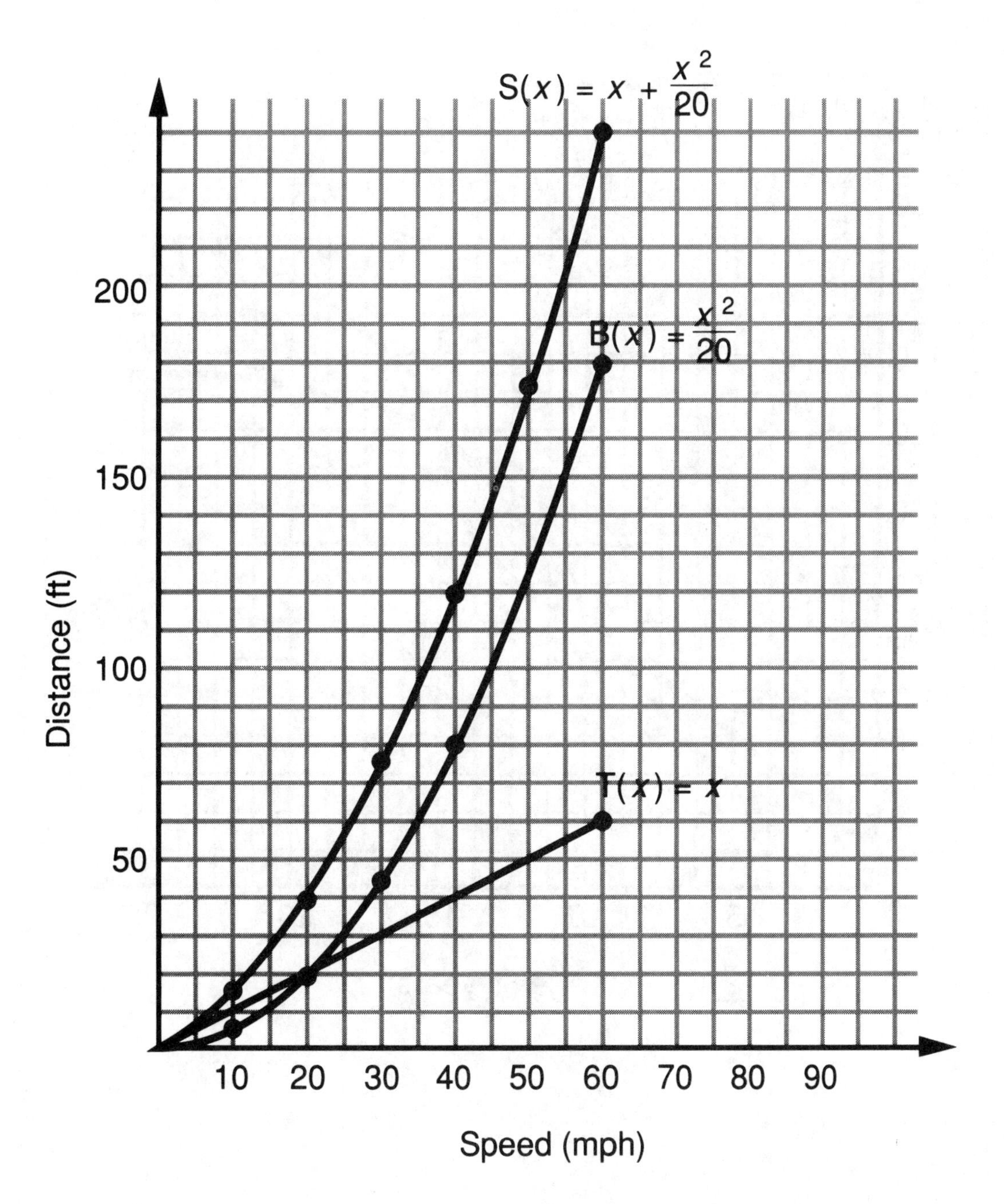

# Lesson 7-2: Questions 19–22

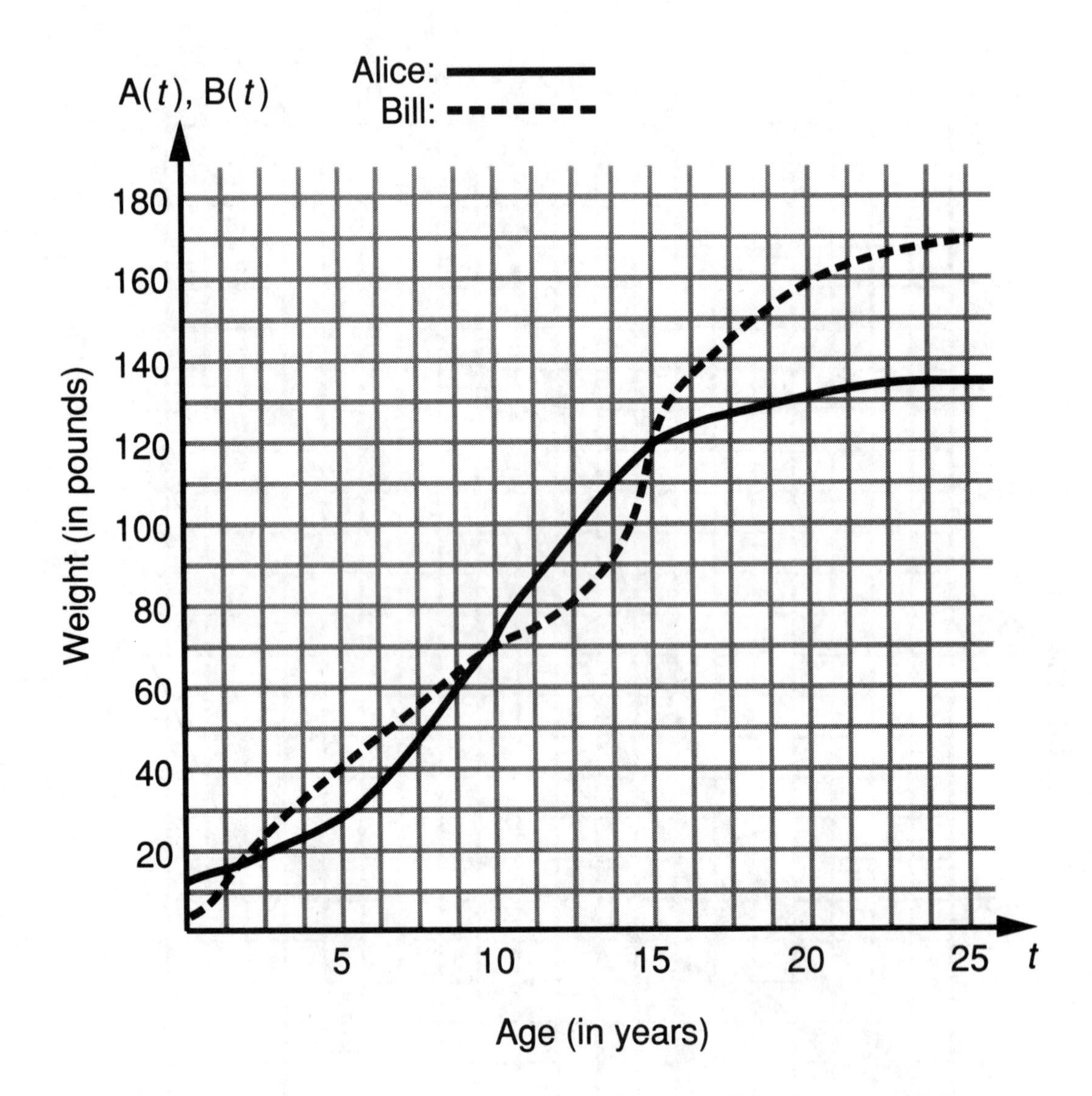

# Cost of Parking a Car from 7:00 p.m. to 1:30 a.m.

| time | number of minutes since 7:00 | cost (in dollars) |
|---|---|---|
| 7:00 – 7:30 | $0 < n \leq 30$ | .75 |
| 7:30 – 8:30 | $30 < n \leq 90$ | .75 + .50 = 1.25 |
| 8:30 – 9:30 | $90 < n \leq 150$ | 1.25 + .50 = 1.75 |
| 9:30 – 10:30 | $150 < n \leq 210$ | 1.75 + .50 = 2.25 |
| 10:30 – 11:30 | $210 < n \leq 270$ | 2.25 + .50 = 2.75 |
| 11:30 – 12:30 | $270 < n \leq 330$ | 2.75 + .50 = 3.25 |
| 12:30 – 1:30 | $330 < n \leq 390$ | 3.25 + .50 = 3.75 |

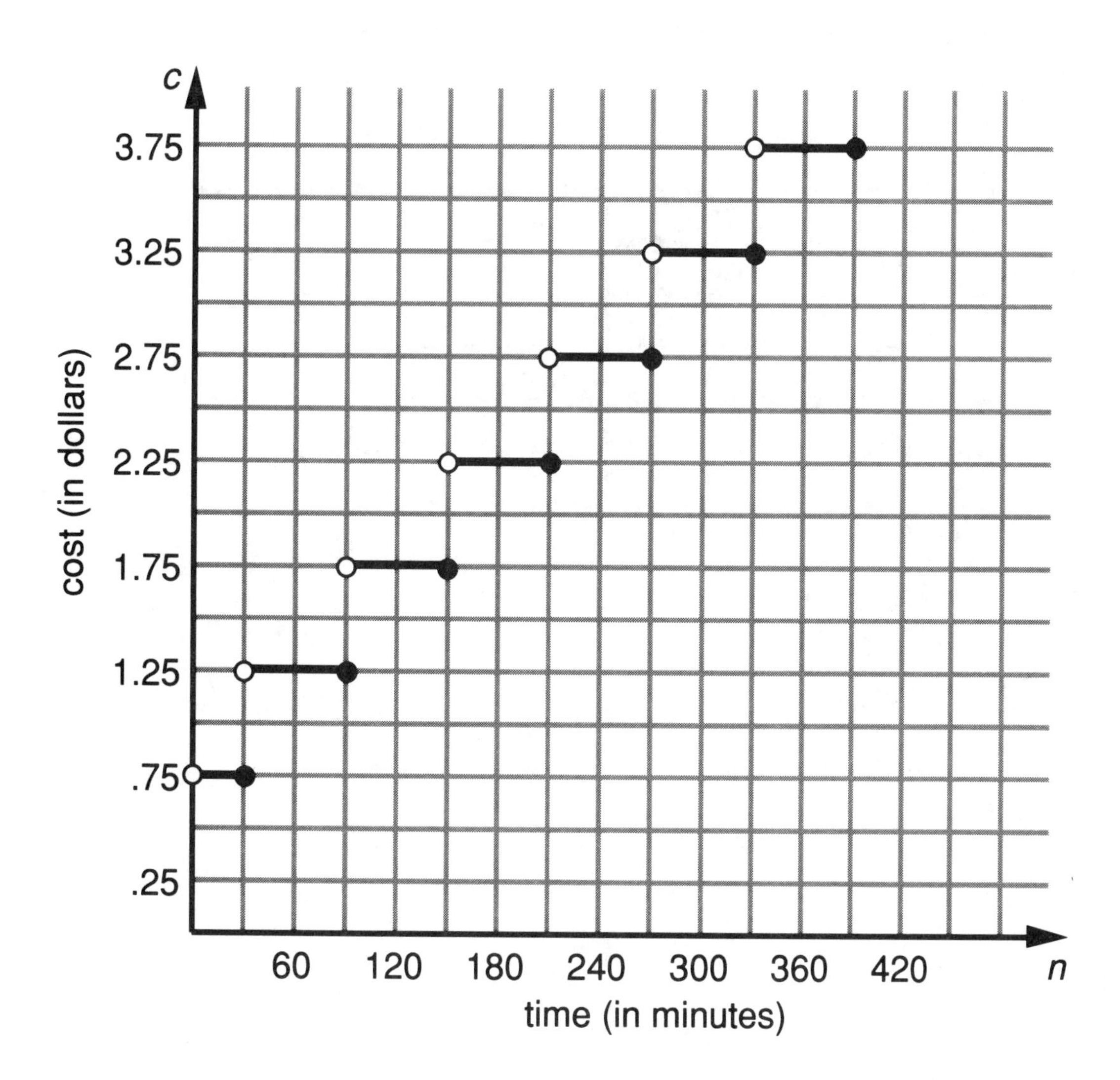

# The Greatest Integer Function
# INT (X) = [x]

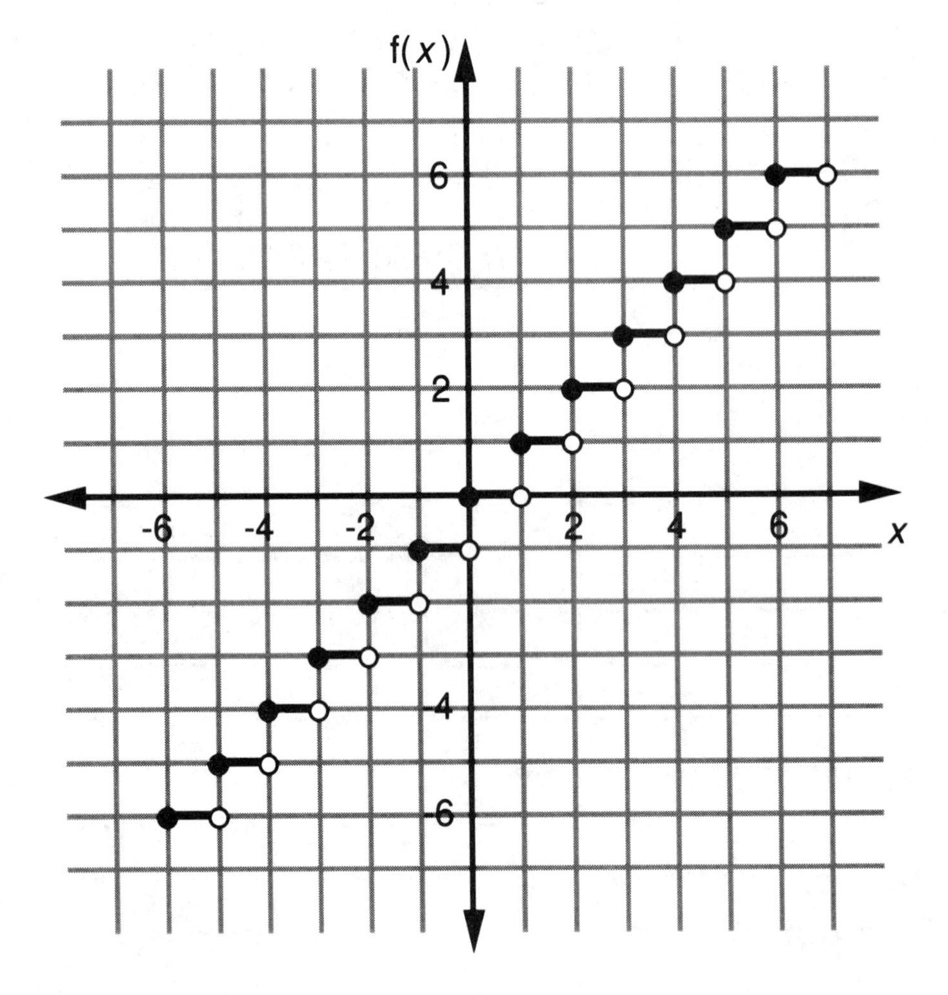

# Graphs of Several Powering Functions

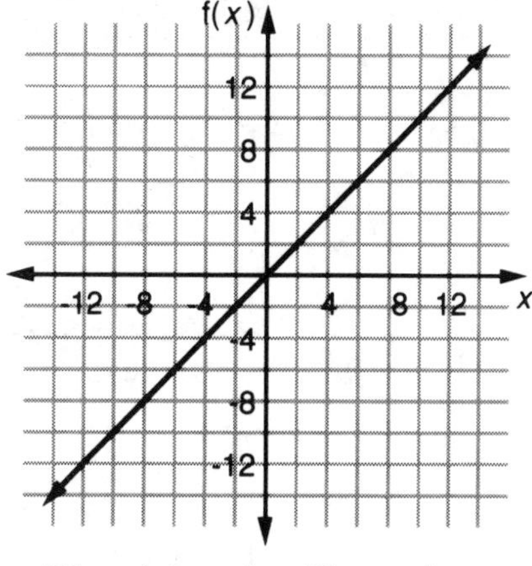


The Identity Function
$f(x) = x$

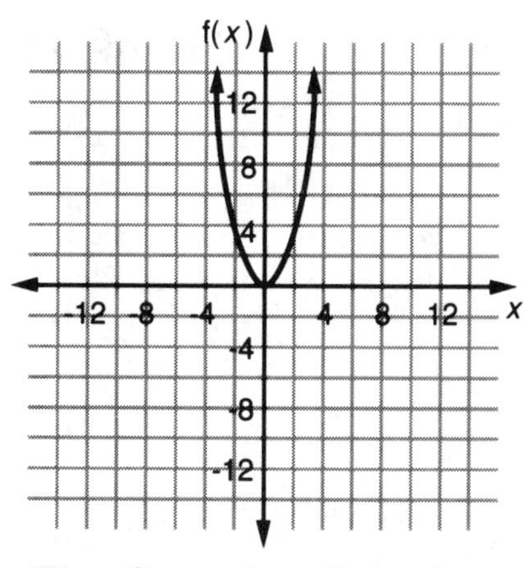


The Squaring Function
$f(x) = x^2$

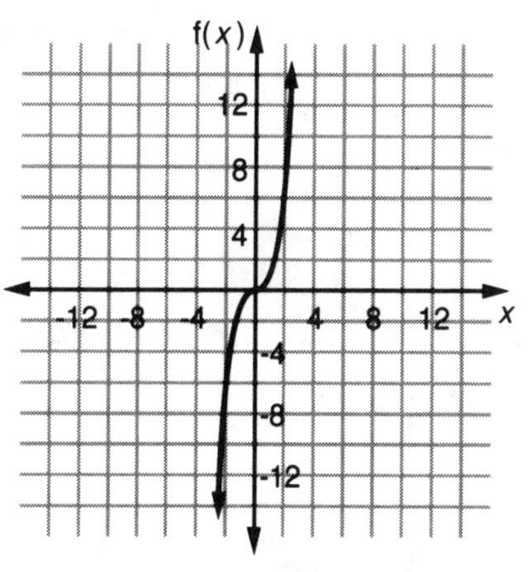


The Cubing Function
$f(x) = x^3$

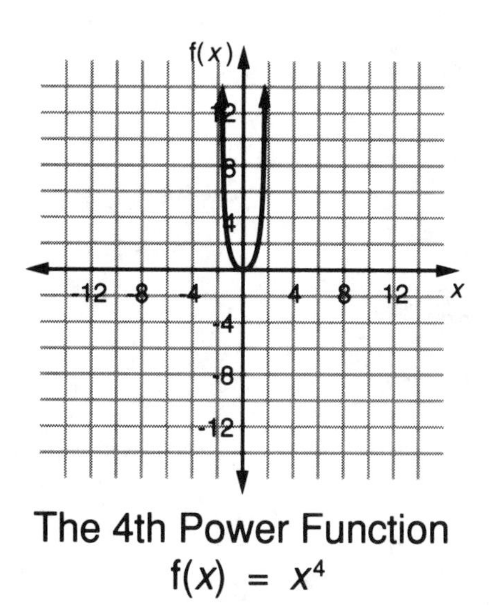


The 4th Power Function
$f(x) = x^4$

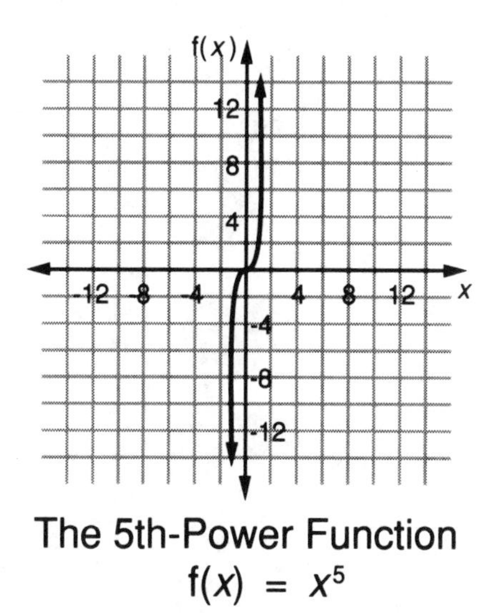


The 5th-Power Function
$f(x) = x^5$

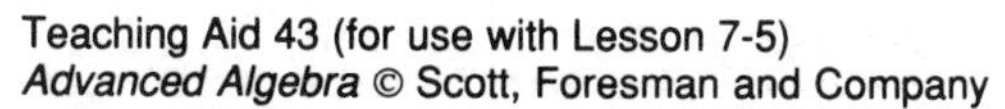

# Graphs of Special Functions

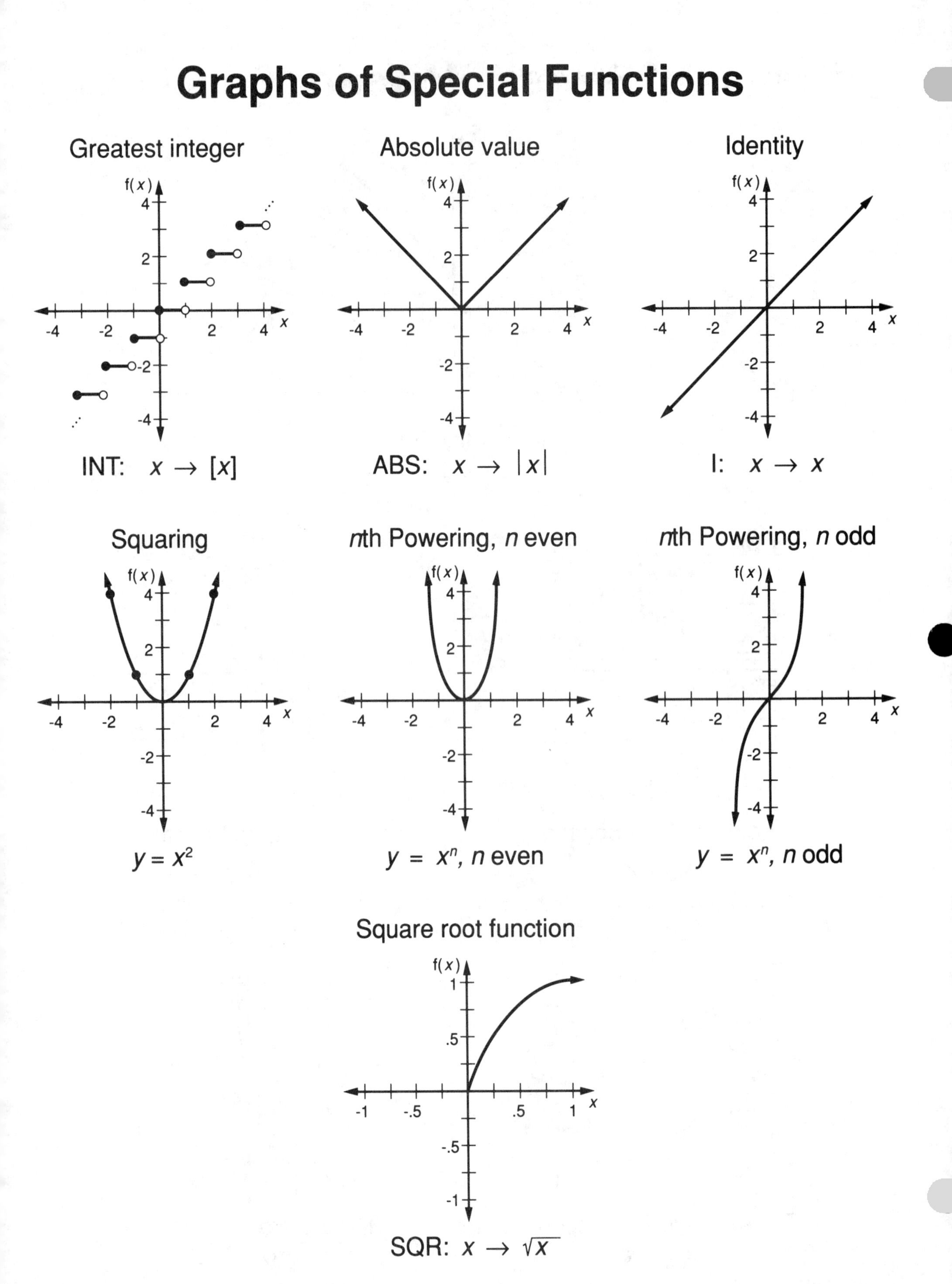

# Main Ideas of Lesson 8-1

**Repeated Multiplication Model for Powering:**
If $b$ is a real number and $n$ is a positive integer, then

$$b^n = \underbrace{b \cdot b \cdot b \cdot \ldots b}_{n \text{ factors}}$$

**Postulate 4: Properties of Powers**
For any nonnegative bases and real exponents, or any nonzero bases and integer exponents:

Product of Powers Property: $b^m \cdot b^n = b^{m+n}$

Power of a Power Property: $(b^m)^n = b^{mn}$

Power of a Product Property: $(ab)^m = a^m b^m$

Quotient of Powers Property: $\frac{b^m}{b^n} = b^{m-n}$

Power of a Quotient Property: $\left(\frac{a}{b}\right)^m = \frac{a^m}{b^m}$

**Zero Exponent Theorem:**
If $b$ is a nonzero real number,

$$b^0 = 1.$$

# Lesson 8-4: Question 33

| | | | |
|---|---|---|---|
| $5^6 =$ | 15,625 | $2^6 =$ | 64 |
| $5^5 =$ | 3,125 | $2^5 =$ | 32 |
| $5^4 =$ | 625 | $2^4 =$ | 16 |
| $5^3 =$ | 125 | $2^3 =$ | 8 |
| $5^2 =$ | 25 | $2^2 =$ | 4 |
| $5^1 =$ | 5 | $2^1 =$ | 2 |
| $5^0 =$ | 1 | $2^0 =$ | 1 |
| $5^{-1} =$ | 0.2 | $2^{-1} =$ | 0.5 |
| $5^{-2} =$ | 0.04 | $2^{-2} =$ | 0.25 |
| $5^{-3} =$ | 0.008 | $2^{-3} =$ | 0.125 |
| $5^{-4} =$ | 0.0016 | $2^{-4} =$ | 0.0625 |
| $5^{-5} =$ | 0.00032 | $2^{-5} =$ | 0.03125 |
| $5^{-6} =$ | 0.000064 | $2^{-6} =$ | 0.015625 |

# Lesson 8-8: Question 35

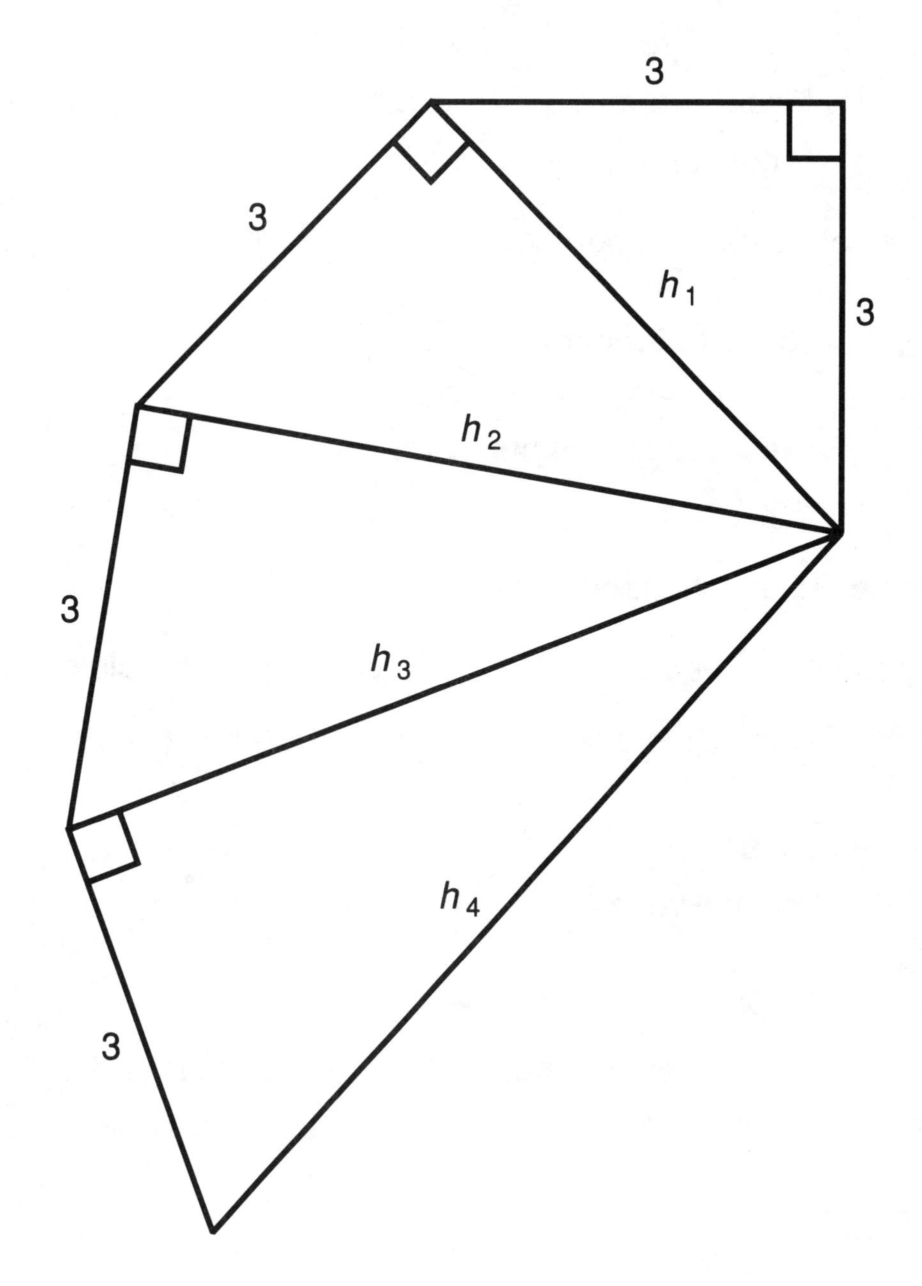

# Properties of Powers and Roots

**For any nonnegative bases and real exponents, or any nonzero bases and integer exponents:**

| | |
|---|---|
| Product of Powers Property | $x^m \cdot x^n = x^{m+n}$ |
| Power of a Power Property | $(x^m)^n = x^{mn}$ |
| Power of a Product Property | $(xy)^n = x^n y^n$ |
| Quotient of Powers Property | $\frac{x^m}{x^n} = x^{m-n}$ |
| Power of a Quotient Property | $\left(\frac{x}{y}\right)^m = \frac{x^m}{y^m}$ |

**For Positive bases and real exponents:**

| | |
|---|---|
| Zero Exponent Theorem | $x^0 = 1$ |
| Negative Exponent Theorem | $x^{-m} = \frac{1}{x^m}$ |
| $\frac{1}{n}$ Exponent Theorem | $x^{1/n} =$ positive solution to $b^n = x$ |
| Root of a Power Theorem | $x^{m/n} = \sqrt[n]{x^m} = (\sqrt[n]{x})^m$ |

**For positive bases:**

| | |
|---|---|
| Root of a Product Property | $\sqrt[n]{xy} = \sqrt[n]{x} \cdot \sqrt[n]{y},\ n > 1$ |

**For real bases and $n \geq 2$:**

| | |
|---|---|
| $n$th Root of $n$th Power Theorem | $\sqrt[n]{x^n} = x$, if $n$ is odd |
| | $\sqrt[n]{x^n} = \lvert x \rvert$, if $n$ is even |

**Formulas:**

| | |
|---|---|
| Compound Interest Formula | $A = P(1 + \frac{r}{n})^{nt}$ |
| Explicit Formula for a Geometric Sequence | $g_n = g_1 r^{n-1}$ |
| Recursive Formula for a Geometric Sequence: | $g_n = rg_{n-1},\ n > 1$ |

# United States Census Results: 1790–1980

$$\begin{cases} P = 13(1.03)^{x-1830} & \text{for } 1790\text{–}1860 \\ P = 63(1.02)^{x-1890} & \text{for } 1870\text{–}1910 \\ P = 151(1.013)^{x-1950} & \text{for } 1920\text{–present} \end{cases}$$

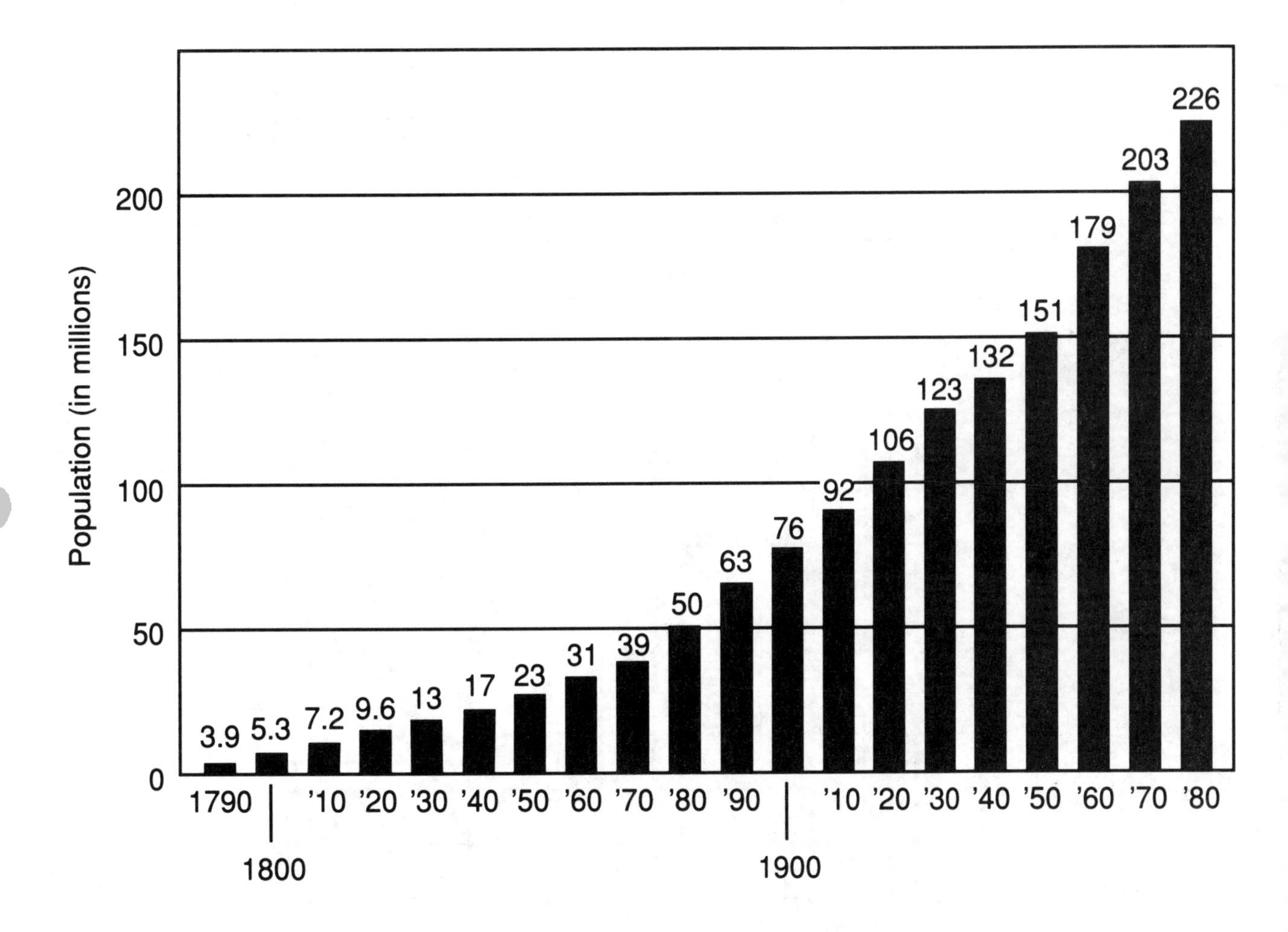


| Year | Population | Decade Growth Factor |
|---|---|---|
| 1920 | 106,020,000 | |
| 1930 | 123,200,000 | 1.162 |
| 1940 | 132,160,000 | 1.073 |
| 1950 | 151,330,000 | 1.145 |
| 1960 | 179,320,000 | 1.185 |
| 1970 | 203,300,000 | 1.134 |
| 1980 | 226,540,000 | 1.114 |

# An Exponential Curve
## $y = 300 \cdot 2^x$

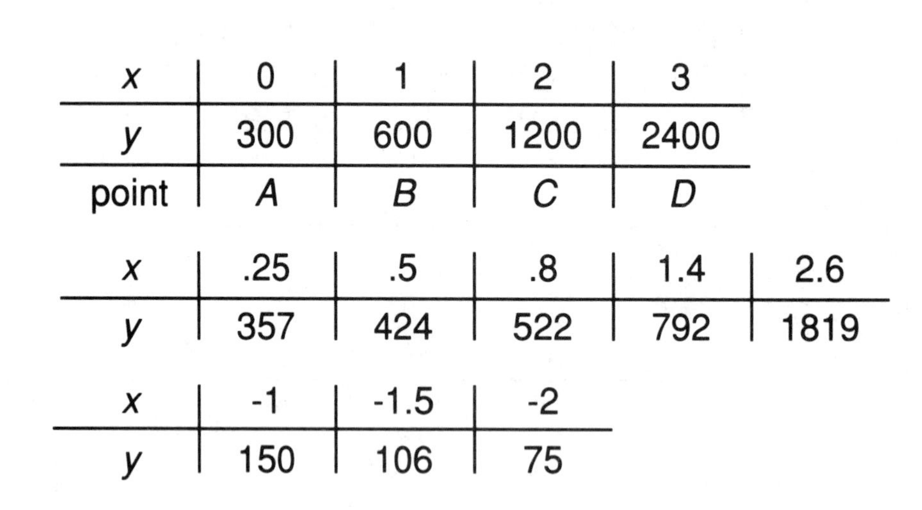

| $x$ | 0 | 1 | 2 | 3 |
|---|---|---|---|---|
| $y$ | 300 | 600 | 1200 | 2400 |
| point | *A* | *B* | *C* | *D* |

| $x$ | .25 | .5 | .8 | 1.4 | 2.6 |
|---|---|---|---|---|---|
| $y$ | 357 | 424 | 522 | 792 | 1819 |

| $x$ | -1 | -1.5 | -2 |
|---|---|---|---|
| $y$ | 150 | 106 | 75 |

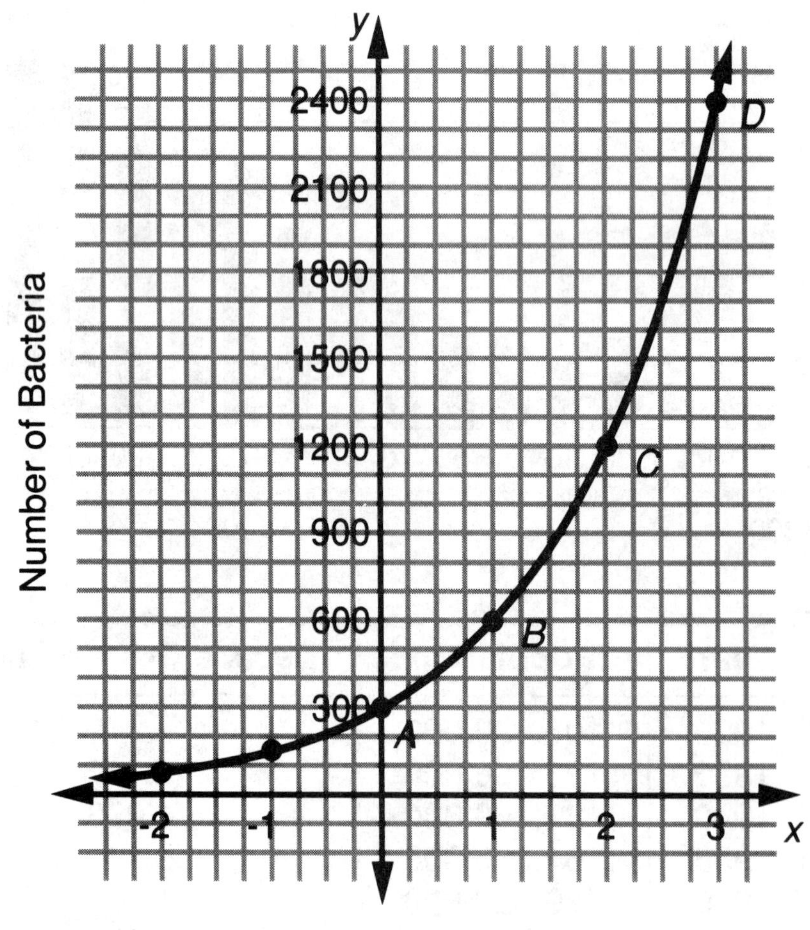

# Lesson 9-2: Example 2
## $y = 100(0.5)^x$

| $x$ | -1 | 0 | 1 | 2 | 3 | 4 |
|---|---|---|---|---|---|---|
| $y$ | 200 | 100 | 50 | 25 | 12.5 | 6.25 |

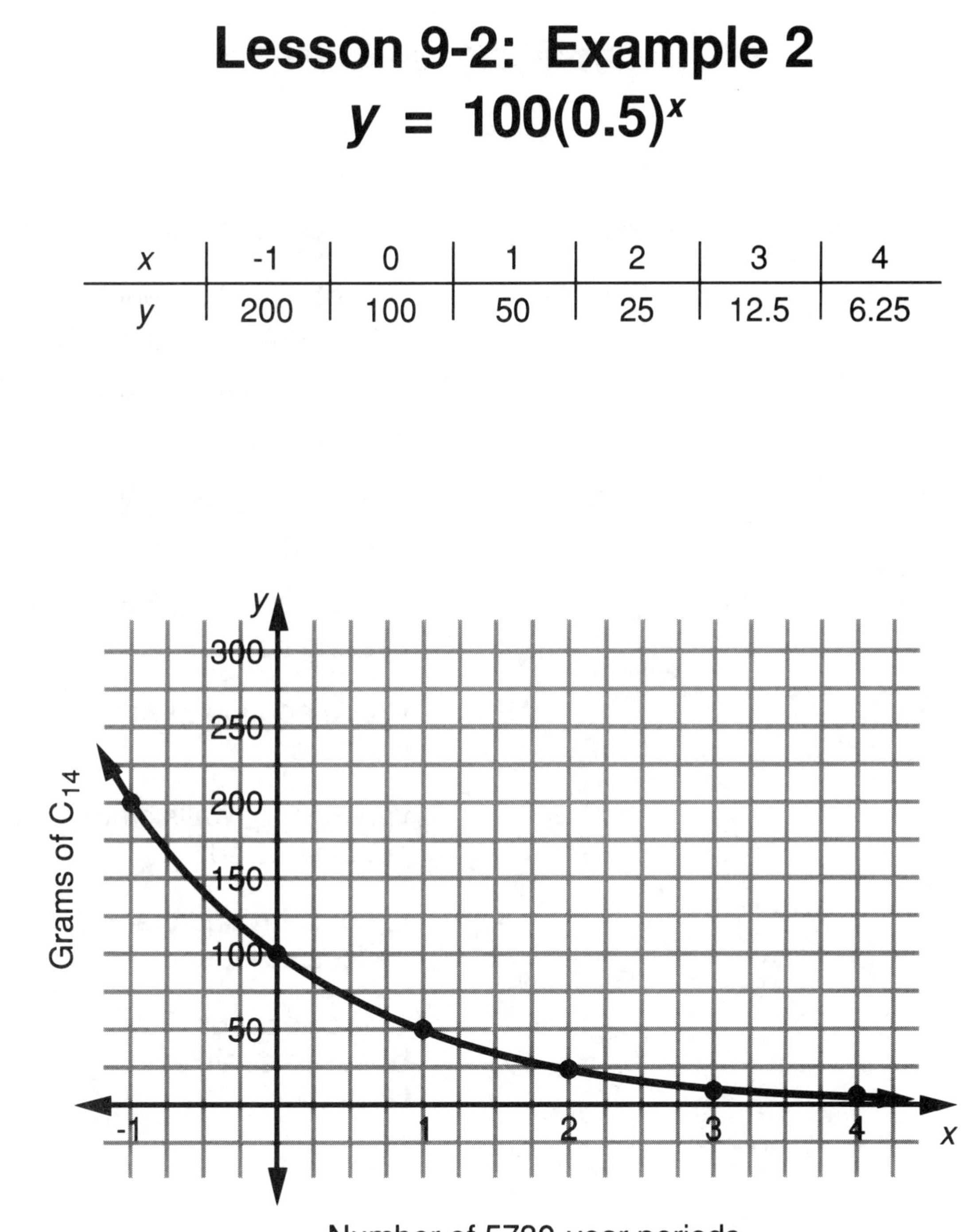

# Richter Magnitudes

| Richter Magnitude | Description |
|---|---|
| 1 | cannot be felt except by instruments |
| 2 | cannot be felt except by instruments |
| 3 | cannot be felt except by instruments |
| 4 | like vibrations from a passing train |
| 5 | strong enough to wake sleepers |
| 6 | very strong; walls crack, people injured |
| 7 | ruinous; ground cracks, houses collapse |
| 8 | very disastrous; few buildings survive; landslides |

# Decibel Scale

| Watts/Square Meter | | Decibels |
|---|---|---|
| $10^{2}$ | jet plane (30 m away) | 140 |
| $10^{1}$ | pain level | 130 |
| $10^{0}$ | amplified rock music (2 m) | 120 |
| $10^{-1}$ | | 110 |
| $10^{-2}$ | noisy kitchen | 100 |
| $10^{-3}$ | heavy traffic | 90 |
| $10^{-4}$ | | 80 |
| $10^{-5}$ | | 70 |
| $10^{-6}$ | normal conversation | 60 |
| $10^{-7}$ | average home | 50 |
| $10^{-8}$ | | 40 |
| $10^{-9}$ | soft whisper | 30 |
| $10^{-10}$ | | 20 |
| $10^{-11}$ | | 10 |
| $10^{-12}$ | barely audible | 0 |

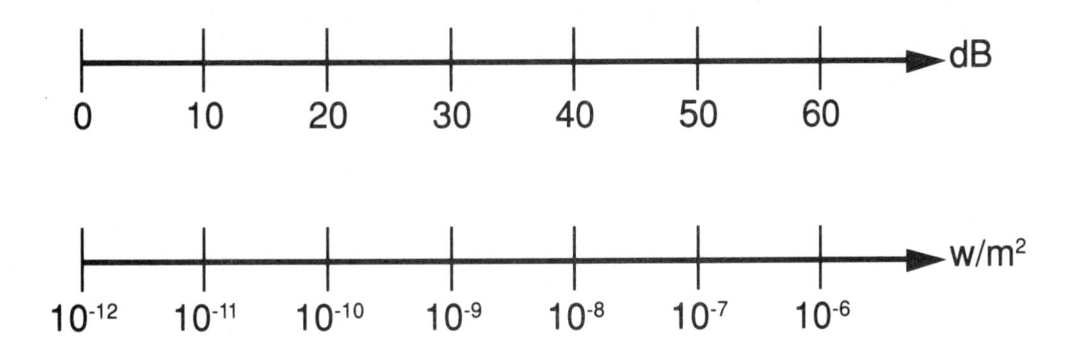

# pH Scale

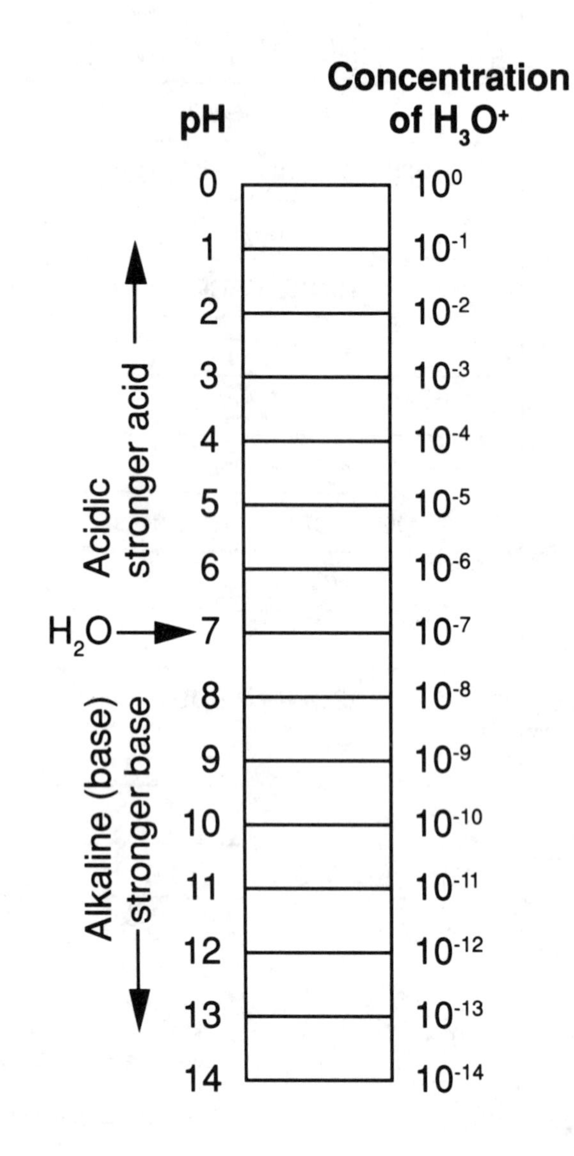

pH
Concentration of $H_3O^+$
0
$10^0$
1
$10^{-1}$
2
$10^{-2}$
3
$10^{-3}$
4
$10^{-4}$
5
$10^{-5}$
6
$10^{-6}$
7
$10^{-7}$
8
$10^{-8}$
9
$10^{-9}$
10
$10^{-10}$
11
$10^{-11}$
12
$10^{-12}$
13
$10^{-13}$
14
$10^{-14}$
Acidic
stronger acid
$H_2O$
Alkaline (base)
stronger base

# The Common Logarithm Function

| $x$ | .1 | 1 | $\sqrt[3]{10}$ ($\approx 2.15$) | $\sqrt{10}$ ($\approx 3.16$) | 5 | 8 | 10 | 31.6* | 100 |
|---|---|---|---|---|---|---|---|---|---|
| $y = \log_{10} x$ | -1 | 0 | $\frac{1}{3}$ | .5 | .7* | .9* | 1 | 1.5 | 2 |

*These values have been rounded to the nearest tenth.

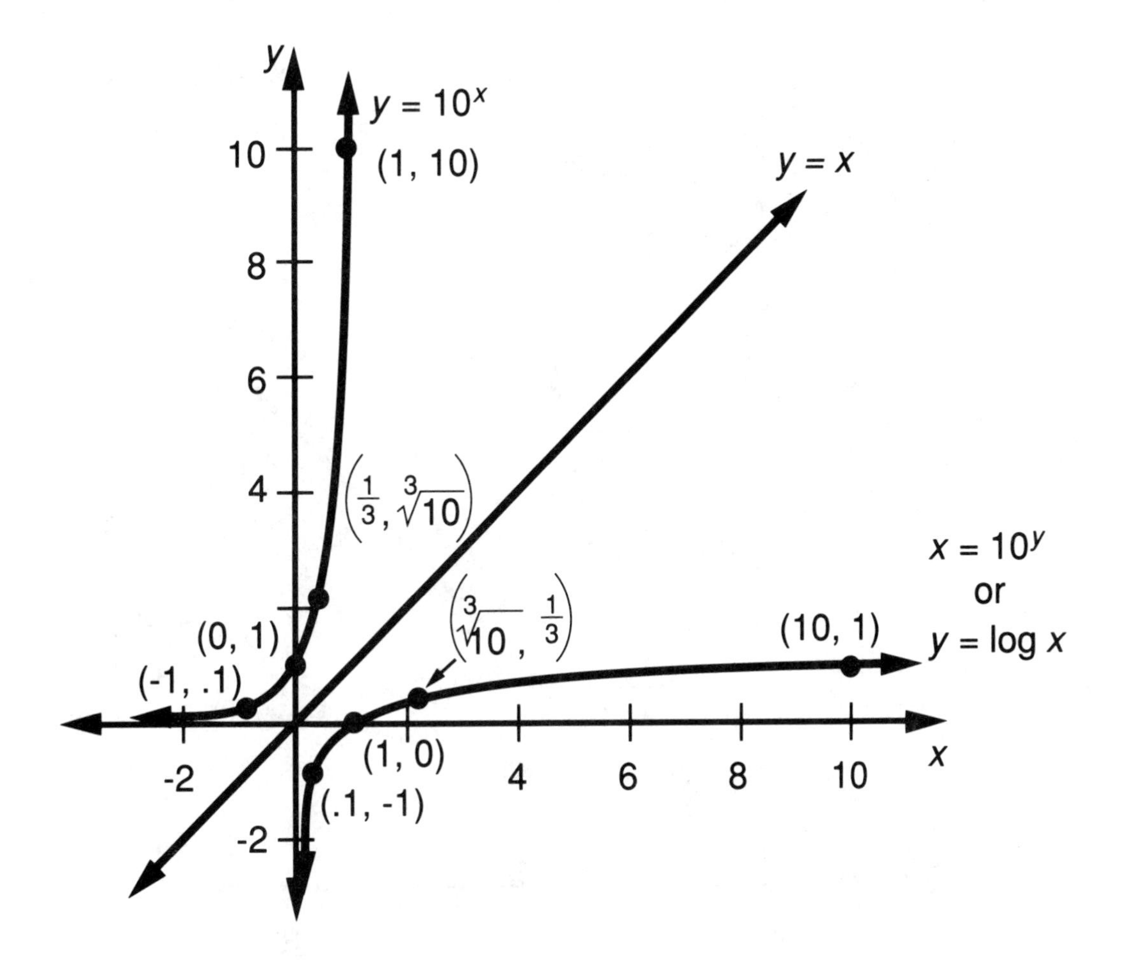

# Base 2 Logarithms

| Exponential Form | | Logarithmic Form |
|---|---|---|
| $2^5 = 32$ | means | $\log_2 32 = 5$ |
| $2^4 = 16$ | means | $\log_2 16 = 4$ |
| $2^3 = 8$ | means | $\log_2 8 = 3$ |
| $2^2 = 4$ | means | $\log_2 4 = 2$ |
| $2^1 = 2$ | means | $\log_2 2 = 1$ |
| $2^0 = 1$ | means | $\log_2 1 = 0$ |
| $2^{-1} = \frac{1}{2}$ | means | $\log_2\left(\frac{1}{2}\right) = -1$ |
| $2^{-2} = \frac{1}{4}$ | means | $\log_2\left(\frac{1}{4}\right) = -2$ |
| $2^{-3} = \frac{1}{8}$ | means | $\log_2\left(\frac{1}{8}\right) = -3$ |

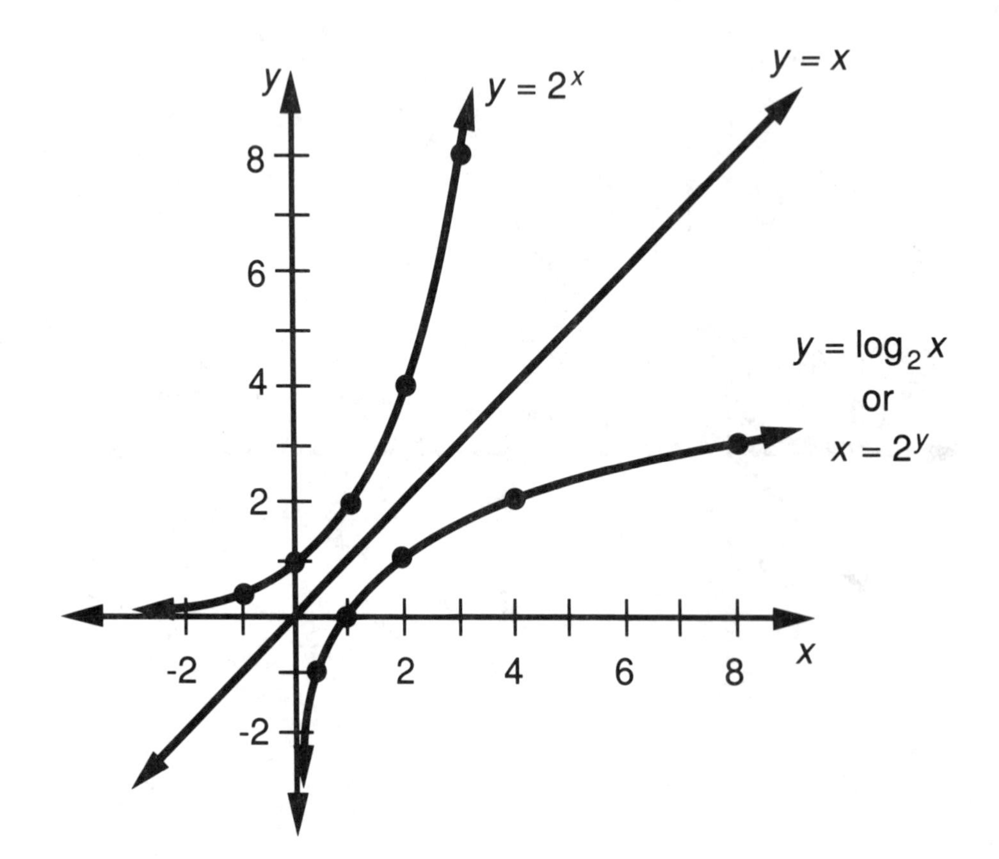

# Logarithm Theorems

**Logarithm Theorem 1:** For any nonzero base *b*,

$$\log_b 1 = 0.$$

**Logarithm Theorem 2:** For any nonzero base *b*,

$$\log_b b^n = n.$$

**Logarithm Theorem 3 (Product Property):** For any nonzero base *b* and positive real numbers *x* and *y*,

$$\log_b (xy) = \log_b x + \log_b y.$$

**Logarithm Theorem 4 (Quotient Property):** For any nonzero base *b* and positive real numbers *x* and *y*,

$$\log_b \left(\frac{x}{y}\right) = \log_b x - \log_b y.$$

**Logarithm Theorem 5 (Powering Property):** For any nonzero base *b* and positive real number *x*,

$$\log_b (x^n) = n \log_b x.$$

# Continuous Compounding

**100% interest**

| $n$ = compoundings per year | | $P(1 + \frac{r}{n})^{nt}$ | $A$ |
|---|---|---|---|
| annually | 1 | $1(1 + \frac{1}{1})^1$ | \$2.00 |
| semi-annually | 2 | $1(1 + \frac{1}{2})^2$ | \$2.25 |
| quarterly | 4 | $1(1 + \frac{1}{4})^4$ | \$2.44141 |
| monthly | 12 | $1(1 + \frac{1}{12})^{12}$ | \$2.61304 |
| daily | 365 | $1(1 + \frac{1}{365})^{365}$ | \$2.71457 |
| hourly | 8760 | $1(1 + \frac{1}{8760})^{8760}$ | \$2.71813 |
| by the second | 31,536,000 | $1(1 + \frac{1}{31,536,000})^{31,536,000}$ | \$2.71830 |

**5% interest**

| compounding method | $P(1 + \frac{r}{n})^{nt}$ | $A$ |
|---|---|---|
| annually | $1(1 + \frac{.05}{1})^1$ | \$1.05 |
| semi-annually | $1(1 + \frac{.05}{2})^2$ | \$1.050625 |
| quarterly | $1(1 + \frac{.05}{4})^4$ | \$1.050945 |
| daily | $1(1 + \frac{.05}{365})^{365}$ | \$1.051267 |
| hourly | $1(1 + \frac{.05}{8760})^{8760}$ | \$1.051271 |

# Natural Logarithms

$e^x = y$

| $x$ | $y$ |
|---|---|
| -1 | 0.37 |
| 0 | 1.00 |
| 1 | 2.72 |
| 1.6 | 4.95 |
| 2 | 7.39 |

$\ln x = y$

| $x$ | $y$ |
|---|---|
| 0.37 | -1 |
| 1.00 | 0 |
| 2.72 | 1 |
| 4.95 | 1.6 |
| 7.39 | 2 |

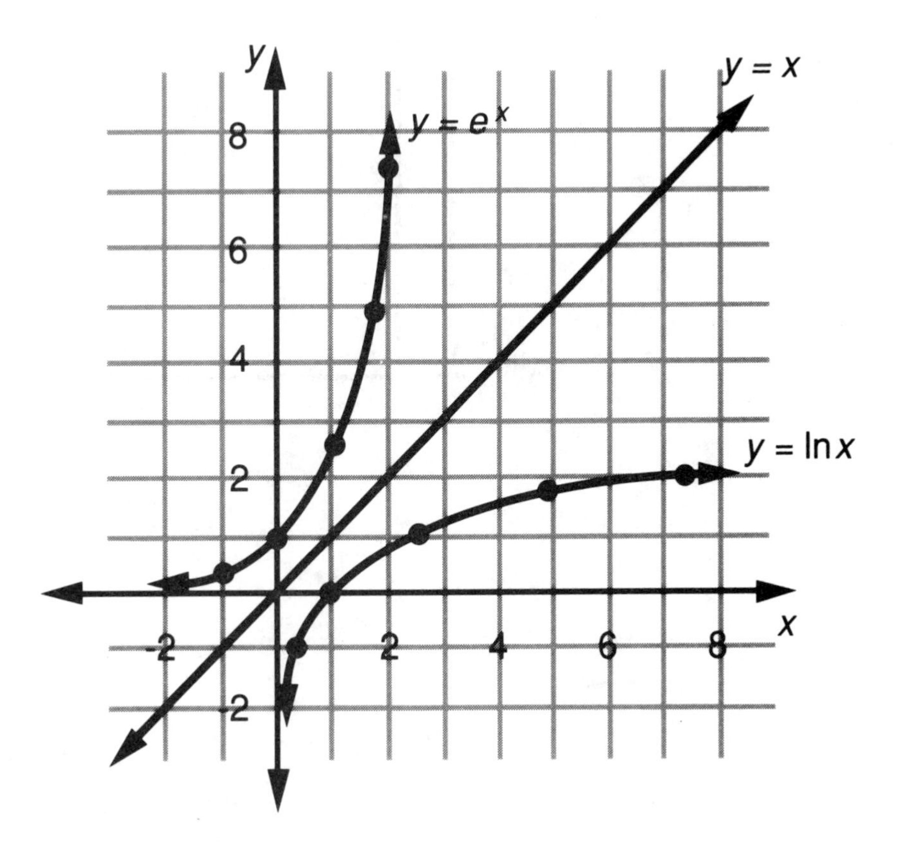

# Lesson 10-2: Additional Example 2

Suppose you have a job building huts in a state park. The ends of the rafters must be pre-cut so that they will form a vertical line with the wall when they are put in place. The front wall is 9 ft high; the back wall is 7 ft high; and the distance between the walls is 5 ft. At what angle θ should you cut the rafters?

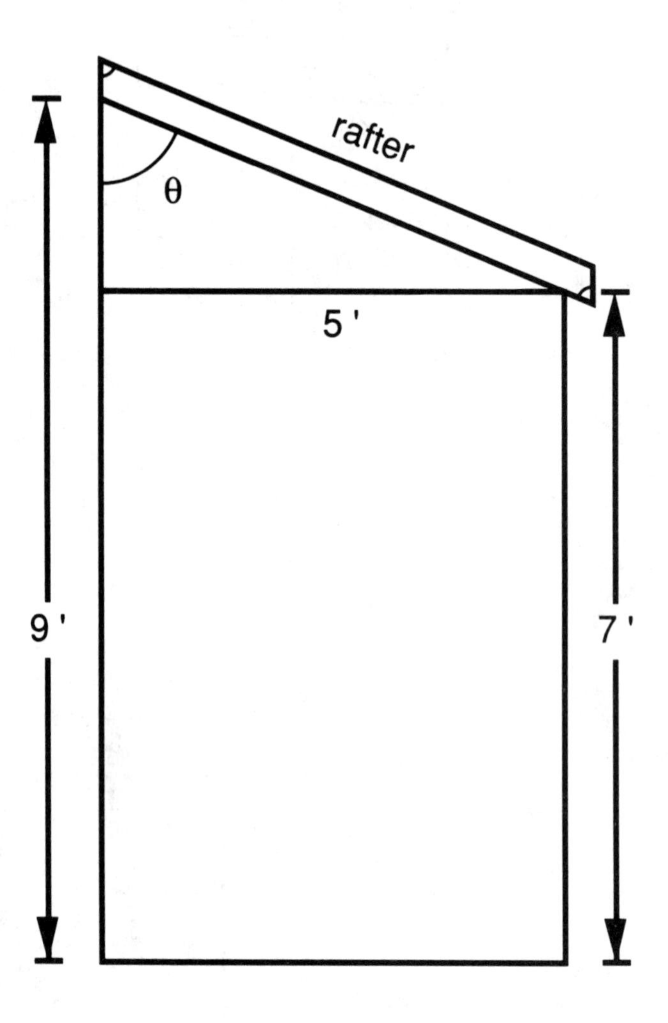

# Lesson 10-2: Additional Example 3

If Earth is assumed to be a sphere, its radius $R$ would be 6400 km. With these assumptions, find the arc length of a degree of longitude at 40° N latitude (approximately the latitude of Philadelphia).

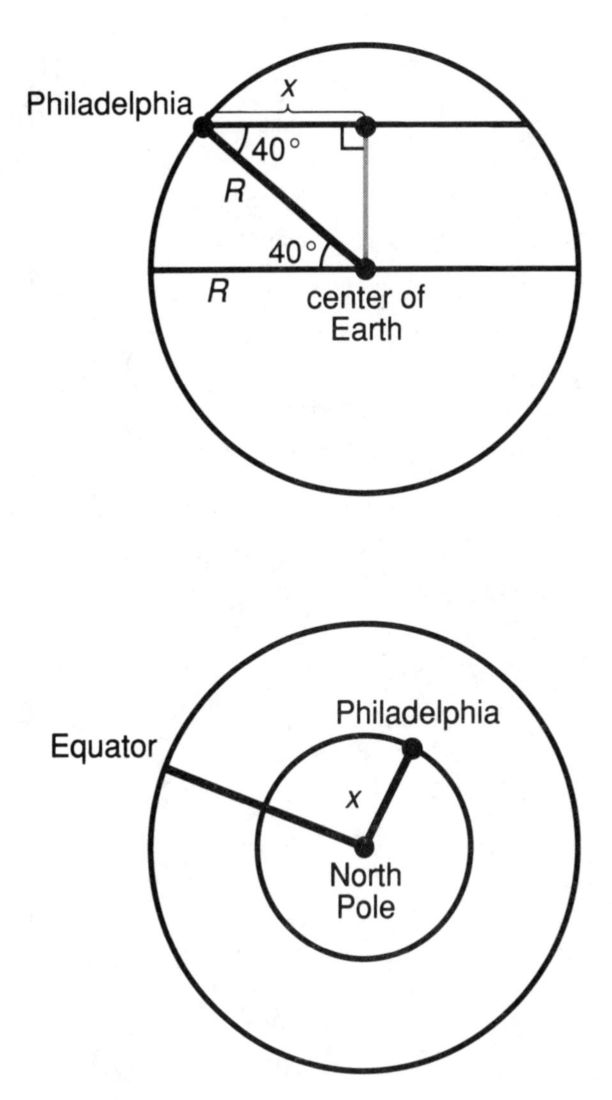

# Cosines and Sines in Quadrants I–IV

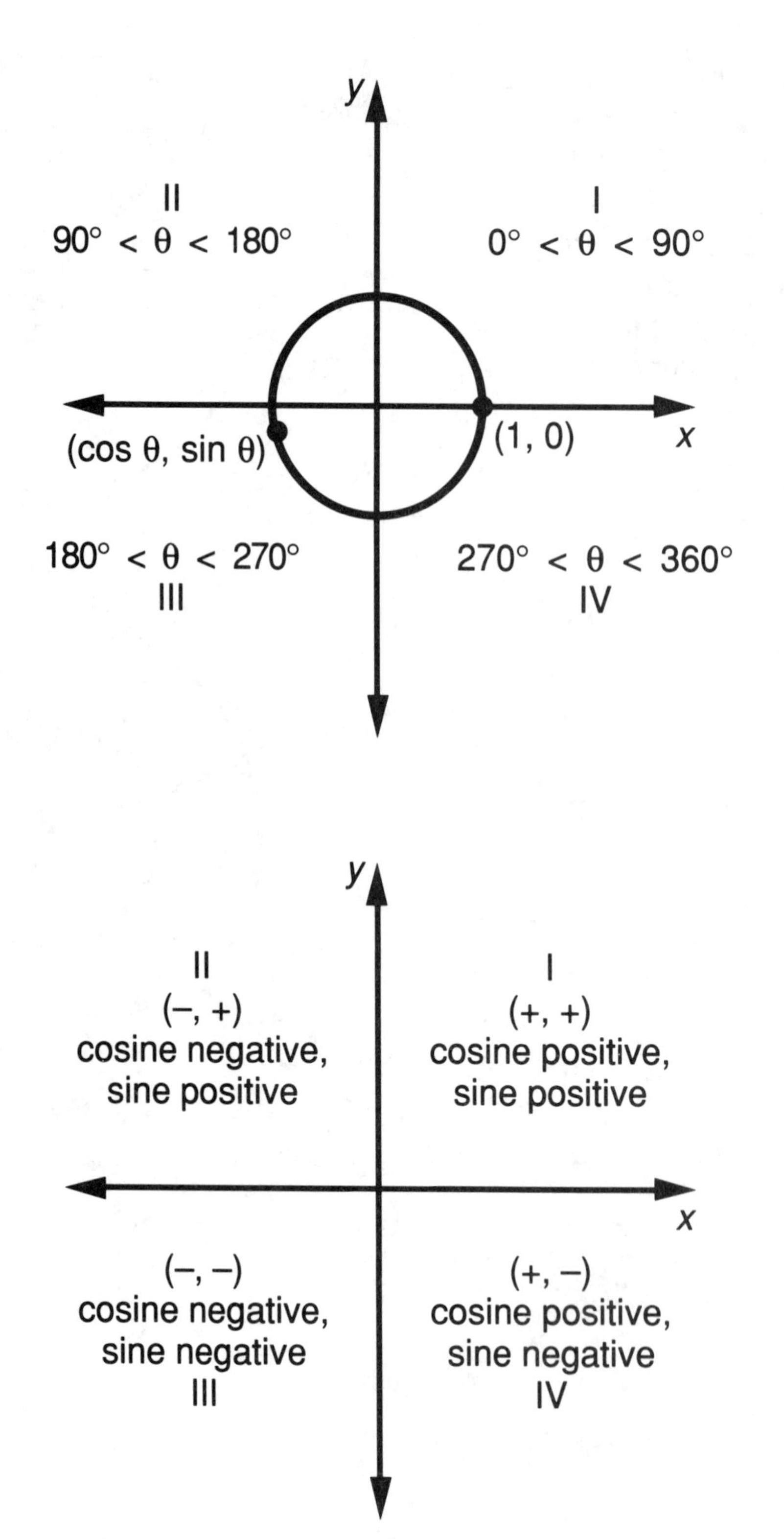

# Images of (1, 0) under $R_\theta$

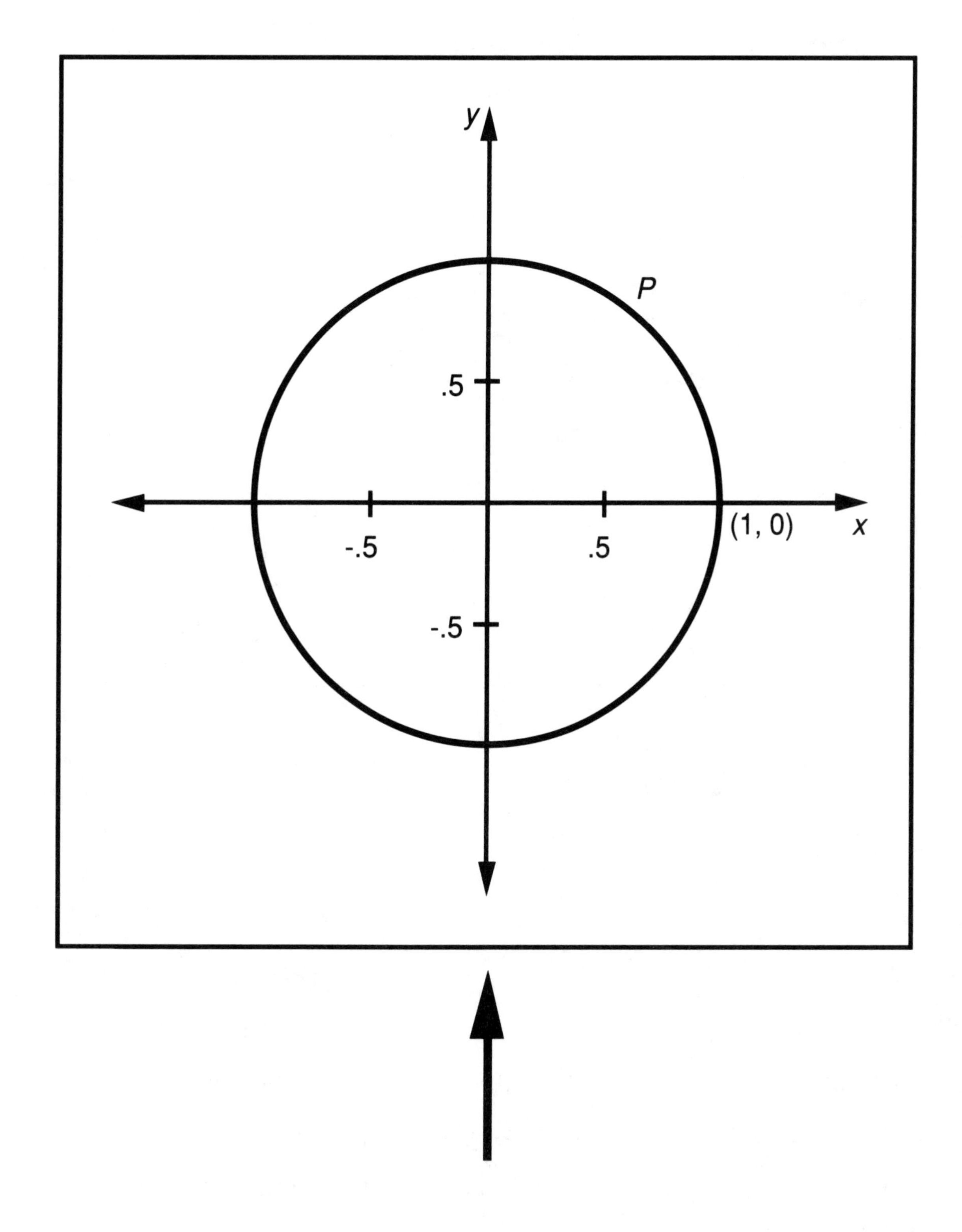

# The Law of Cosines

**In any $\triangle ABC$, $c^2 = a^2 + b^2 - 2ab \cos C$.**

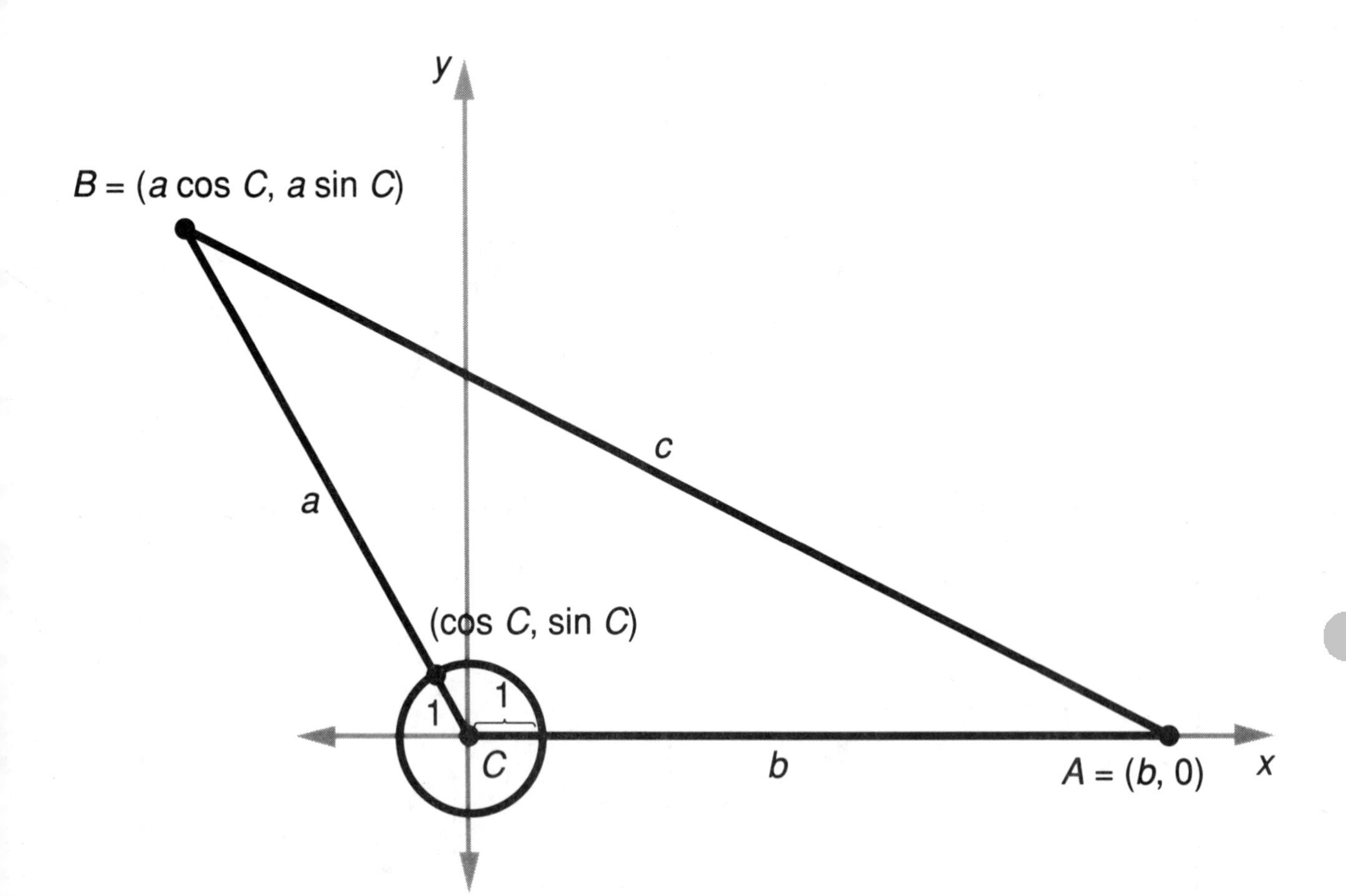


**Proof**

| | |
|---|---|
| $c = \sqrt{(x_2 - x_1)^2 + (y_2 - y_1)^2}$ | Distance Formula |
| $c^2 = (x_2 - x_1)^2 + (y_2 - y_1)^2$ | squaring both sides |
| $c^2 = (a \cos C - b)^2 + (a \sin C - 0)^2$ | substitution |
| $c^2 = a^2(\cos C)^2 - 2ab \cos C + b^2 + a^2(\sin C)^2$ | expansion |
| $c^2 = a^2(\cos C)^2 + a^2(\sin C)^2 + b^2 - 2ab \cos C$ | Commutative Property of + |
| $c^2 = a^2((\cos C)^2 + (\sin C)^2) + b^2 - 2ab \cos C$ | Distributive Postulate |
| $c^2 = a^2 + b^2 - 2ab \cos C$ | Pythagorean Identity |

# Lesson 10-6: Extension

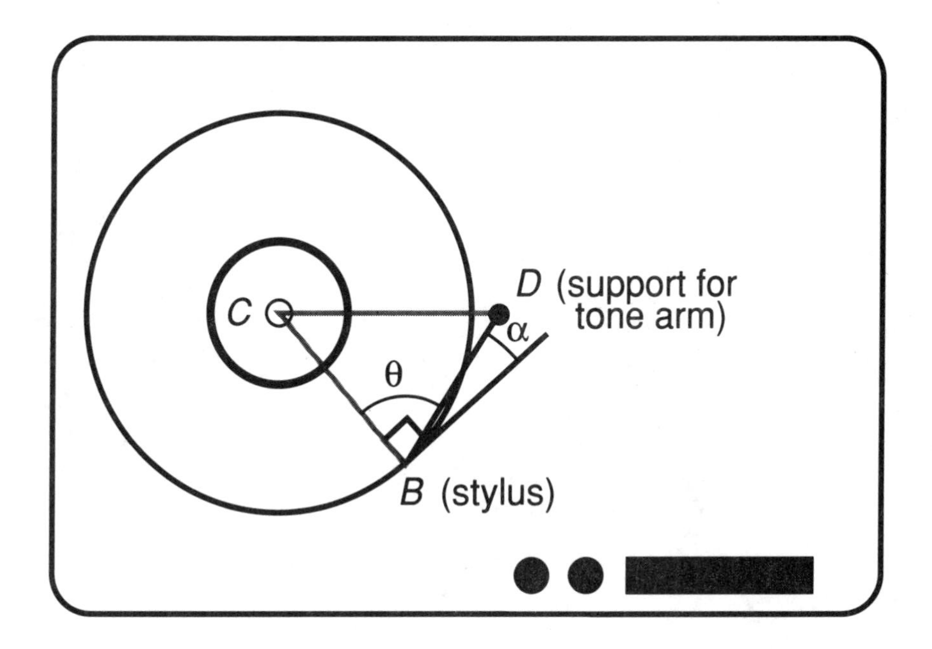


The *tracking-angle error* of a record player is the ratio $\frac{\alpha}{CB}$, where $\alpha$ is the measure in degrees of the angle between the center line and the tangent to the record groove at the stylus, and *CB* is the distance in inches from the stylus to the center of the record. Supppose that the tone arm ($\overline{BD}$) is straight and supported at a point 8" from the center of a record and 8.25" from the stylus. Find the tracking-angle error when the stylus is at the end of a 12" (diameter) record.

# Lesson 10-7: Question 24

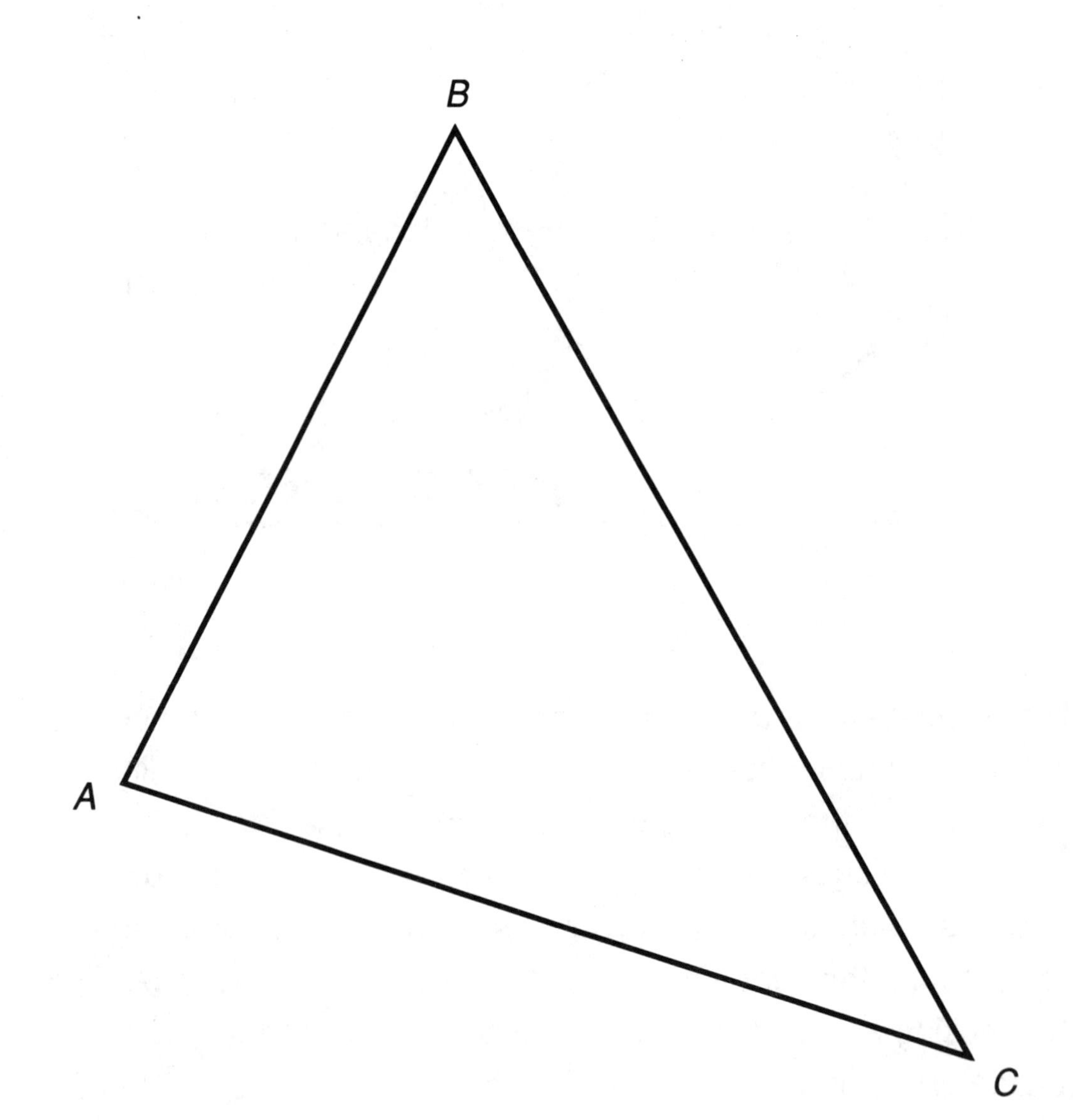

# Lesson 10-7: Additional Example 3

Two Coast Guard ships *S* and *T* pick up distress signals from a third ship *U*. Their instruments determine the direction of *U* but not the distance to *U*. Suppose *U* is 34° south of east from *S*, and 20° south of east from *T*; *S* and *T* know they are 10 km apart with *S* being 43° east of north from *T*.

a. How far is each ship from *U*?

b. If *S* can travel at 27 km/hr and *T* at 30 km/hr, which ship can get to *U* first?

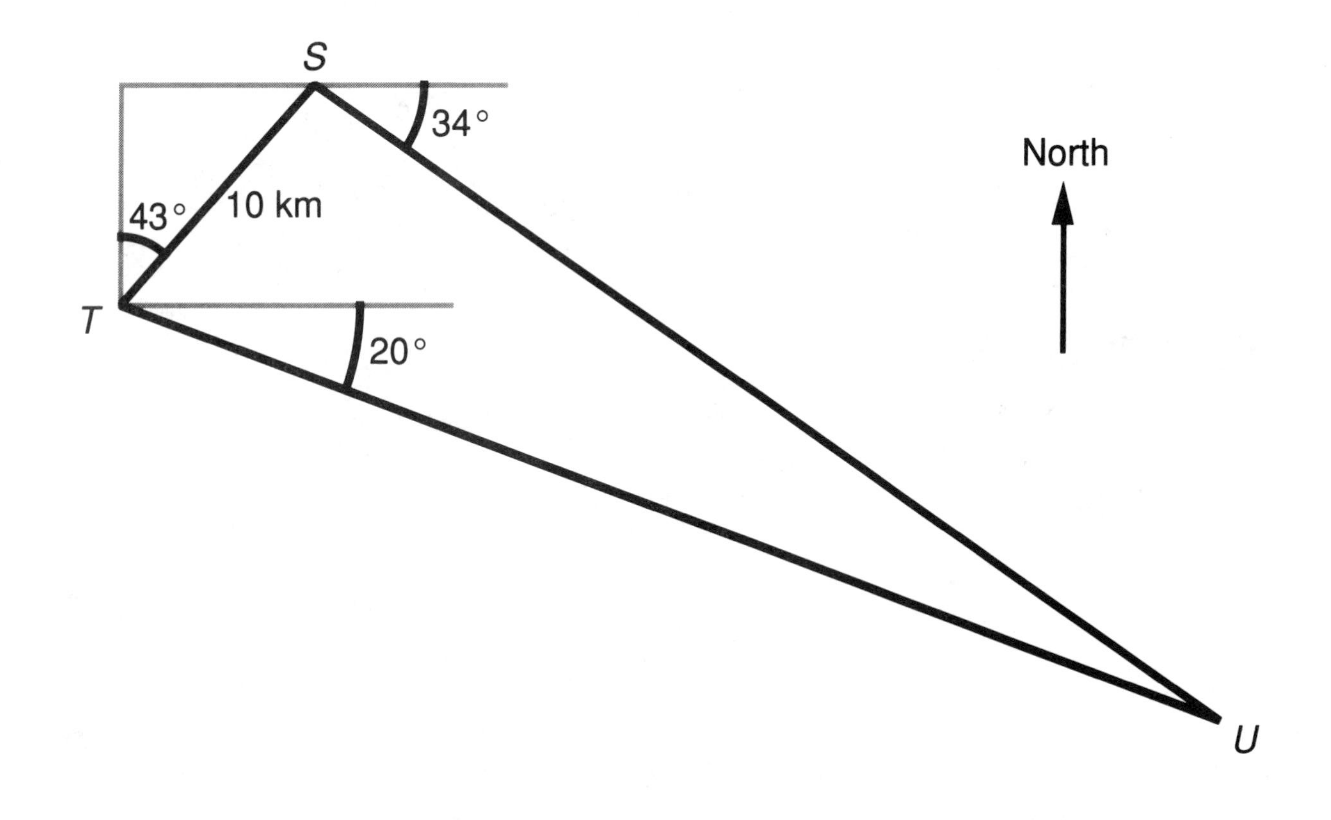

# Some Trigonometric Properties

**For all θ:**

| | |
|---|---|
| Complements Theorem | $\sin\theta = \cos(90° - \theta)$<br>$\cos\theta = \sin(90° - \theta)$ |
| Supplements Theorem | $\sin\theta = \sin(180° - \theta)$ |
| Pythagorean Identity | $(\cos\theta)^2 + (\sin\theta)^2 = 1$ |
| Exact Value Theorem | $\sin 30° = \cos 60° = \frac{1}{2}$<br>$\sin 45° = \cos 45° = \frac{\sqrt{2}}{2}$<br>$\sin 60° = \cos 30° = \frac{\sqrt{3}}{2}$ |

**In any triangle *ABC*:**

| | |
|---|---|
| Law of Cosines | $c^2 = a^2 + b^2 - 2ab\cos C$ |
| Law of Sines | $\frac{\sin A}{a} = \frac{\sin B}{a} = \frac{\sin C}{a}$ |

# Population of Manhattan Island Over Past 100 Years

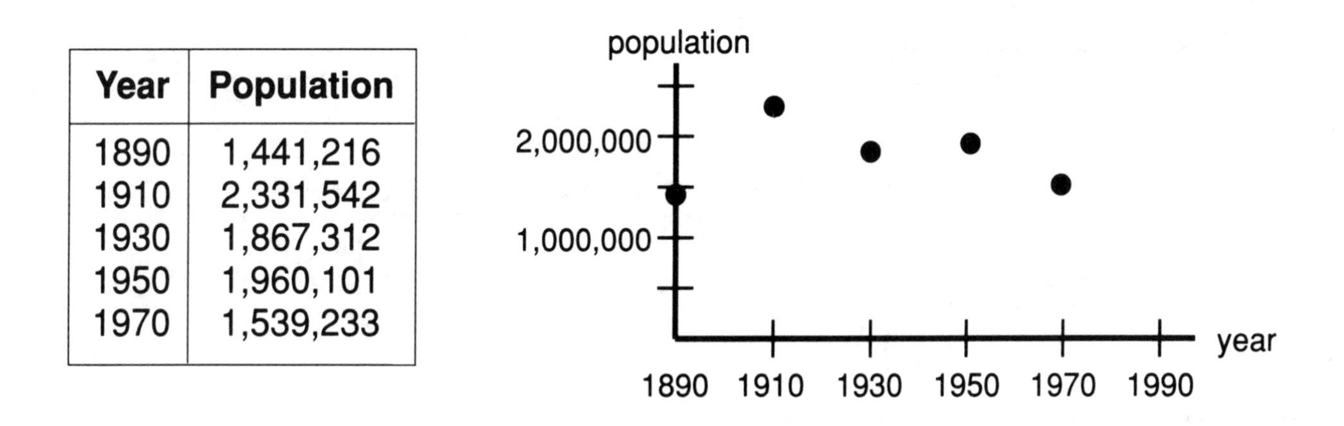

| Year | Population |
|---|---|
| 1890 | 1,441,216 |
| 1910 | 2,331,542 |
| 1930 | 1,867,312 |
| 1950 | 1,960,101 |
| 1970 | 1,539,233 |



$$P(x) = \frac{-37}{3}x^4 + \frac{317}{3}x^3 - \frac{1789}{6}x^2 + \frac{1763}{6}x + 144$$

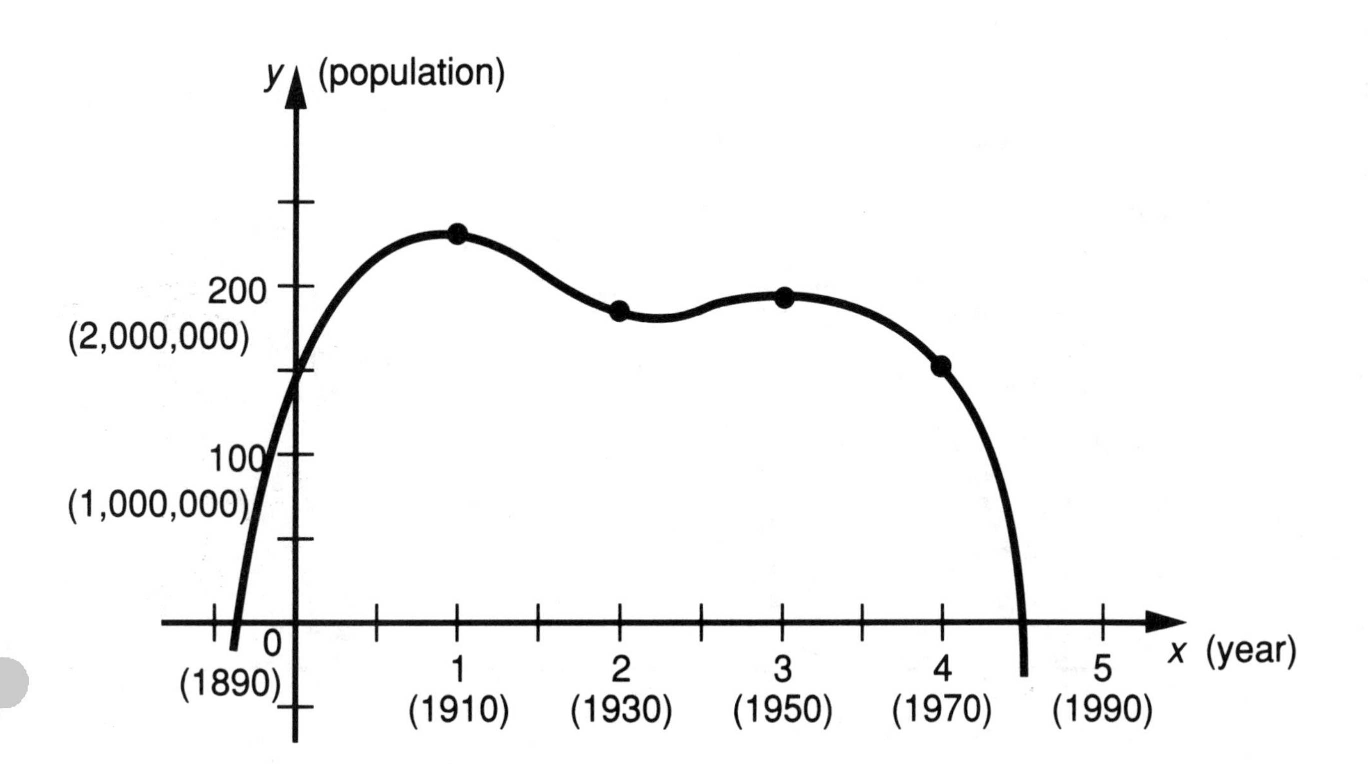

# Lesson 11-2: Example 3

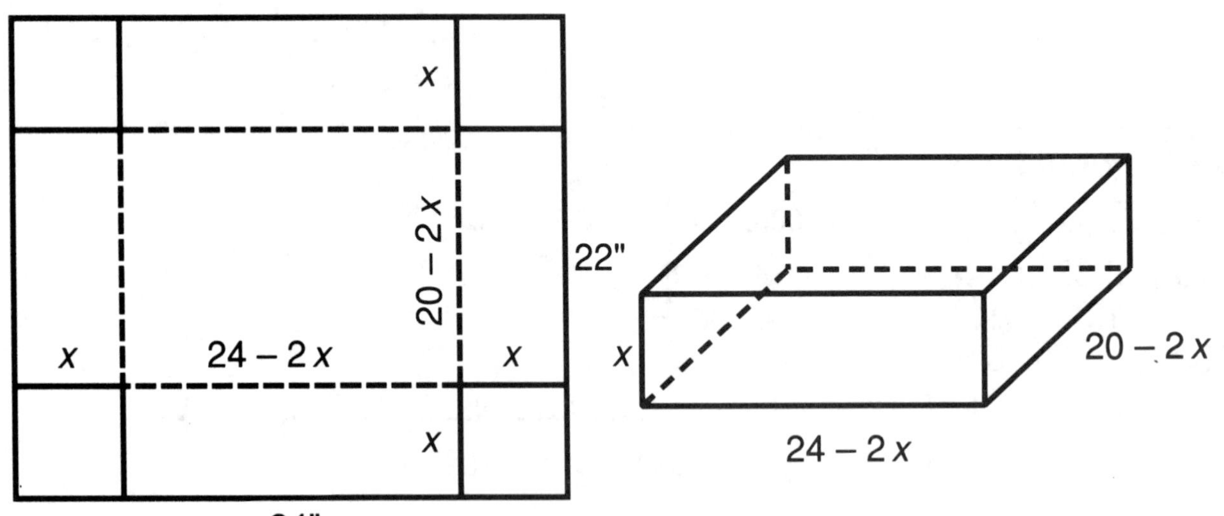


$$V(x) = (24 - 2x)x(20 - 2x)$$
$$V(x) = (24x - 2x^2)(20 - 2x)$$
$$V(x) = 480x - 48x^2 - 40x^2 + 4x^3$$
$$V(x) = 4x^3 - 88x^2 + 480x$$

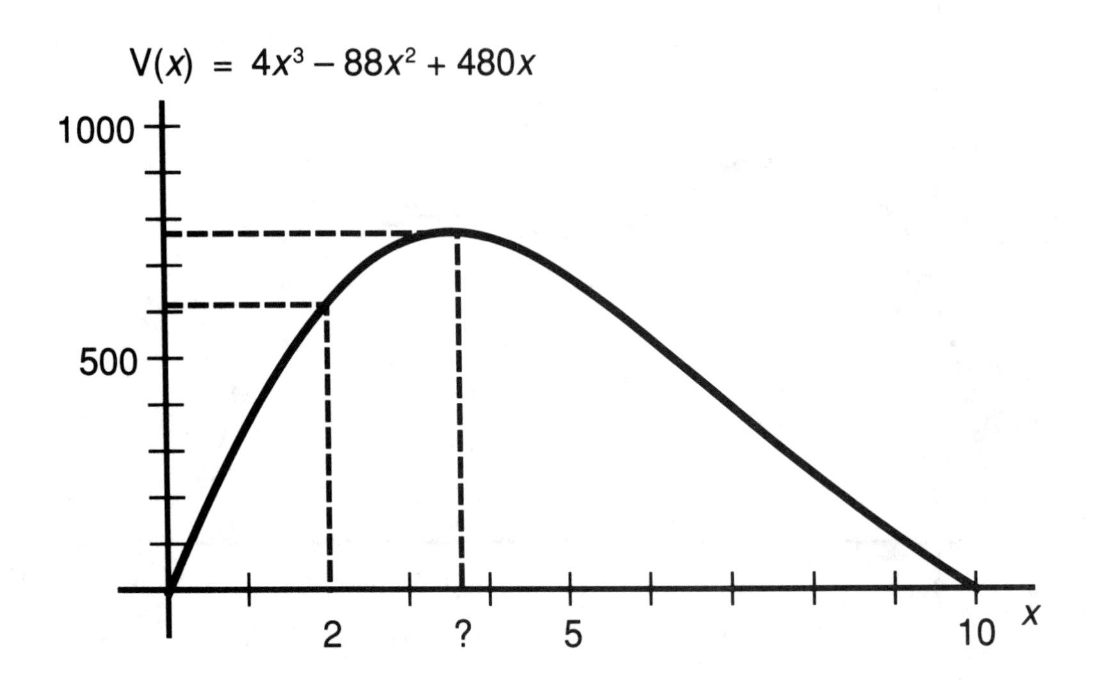

# Polynomial Factoring Patterns

**Perfect Square Trinomial Patterns:**

For all $a$ and $b$,

$$a^2 + 2ab + b^2 = (a + b)^2$$

and

$$a^2 - 2ab + b^2 = (a - b)^2.$$

**Difference of Squares Pattern:**

For all $a$ and $b$,

$$a^2 - b^2 = (a + b)(a - b).$$

**Sum of Cubes Pattern:**

For all $a$ and $b$,

$$a^3 + b^3 = (a + b)(a^2 - ab + b^3).$$

**Difference of Cubes Pattern:**

For all $a$ and $b$,

$$a^3 - b^3 = (a - b)(a^2 + ab + b^3).$$

# Lesson 11-4: Example 4

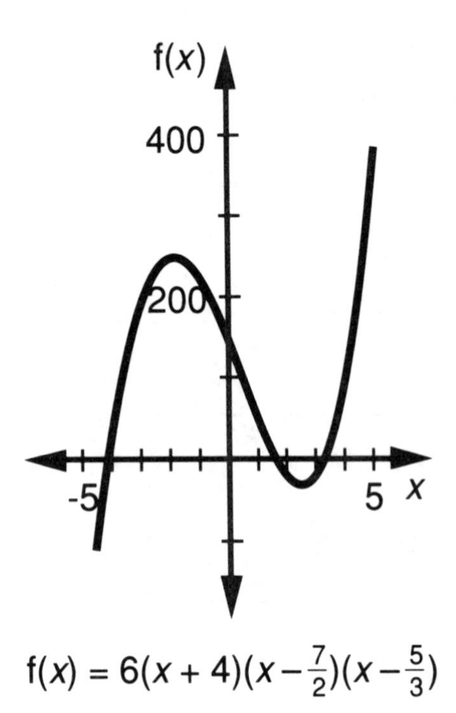


$f(x) = 6(x + 4)(x - \frac{7}{2})(x - \frac{5}{3})$

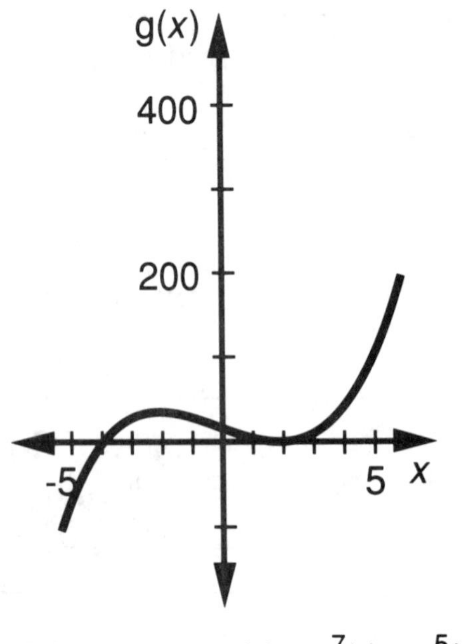


$g(x) = x(x + 4)(x - \frac{7}{2})(x - \frac{5}{3})$

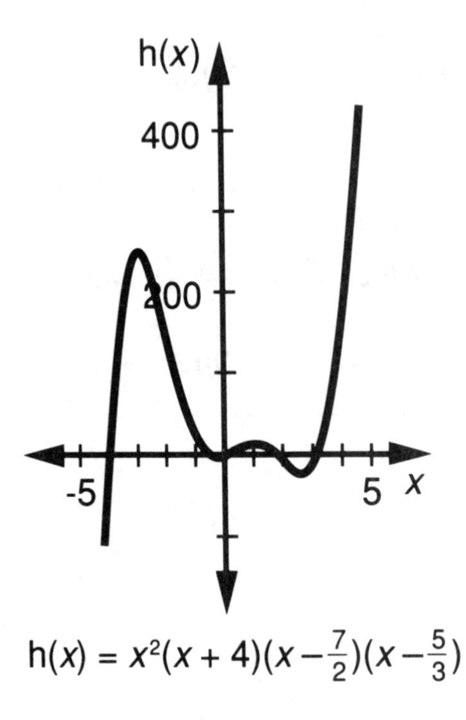


$h(x) = x^2(x + 4)(x - \frac{7}{2})(x - \frac{5}{3})$

# Lesson 11-5: Example 1

$$P(x) = 10x^4 + 15x^3 + 14x^2 + 20x - 78$$

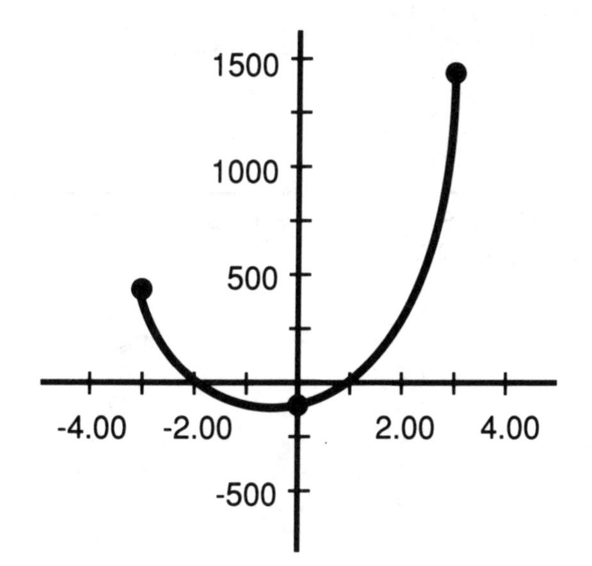


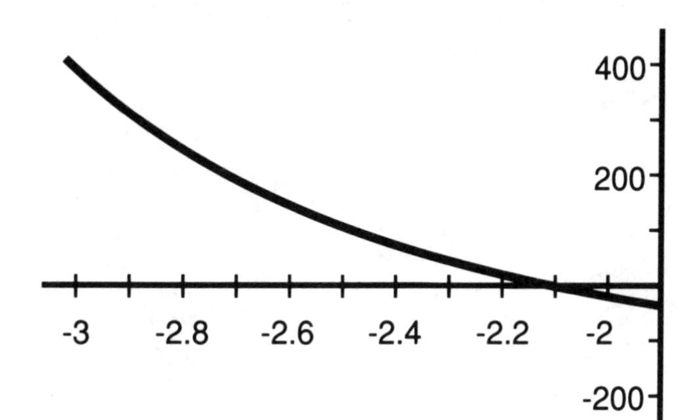


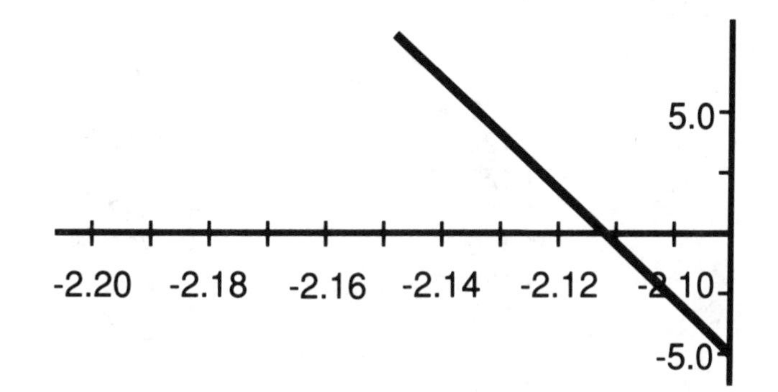

# Lesson 11-5: Example 2

```
 10 REM PROGRAM TO PRINT TABLE OF FUNCTIONAL VALUES
 20 INPUT "ENDPOINTS A AND B OF DOMAIN", A, B
 30 INPUT "STEP SIZE"; C
 40 PRINT "X", "Y"
 50 FOR X = A TO B STEP C
 60      REM TYPE IN YOUR OWN FUNCTION AT LINE 70
 70      Y =
 80      PRINT X, Y
 90 NEXT X
100 END
```

---

```
ENDPOINTS A AND B OF DOMAIN? 1, 2
STEP SIZE? 0.1
          X              Y
          1              -19
          1.1              -4.454
          1.2              12.816
          1.3              33.176
          1.4              57.016
          1.5              84.75
          1.6             116.816
          1.7             153.676
          1.8             195.816
          1.9             243.746
          2.0             298
```

---

```
ENDPOINTS A AND B OF DOMAIN? 1.1, 1.2
STEP SIZE? 0.01
          X              Y
          1.1            -4.454
          1.11           -2.85543
          1.12           -1.22929
          1.13             .424791
          1.14            2.10716
          1.15            3.81819
          1.16            5.55823
          1.17            7.32767
          1.18            9.12686
          1.19           10.9562
          1.20           12.816
```

---

```
ENDPOINTS A AND B OF DOMAIN? 1.12, 1.13
STEP SIZE? 0.001
          X              Y
          1.12           -1.22929
          1.121          -1.06514
          1.122           -.900717
          1.123           -.736012
          1.124           -.571027
          1.125           -.405762
          1.126           -.240215
          1.127           -.074386
          1.128            .091724
          1.129            .258116
          1.13             .424791
```

# Theorems of Lesson 11-6

**The Fundamental Theorem of Algebra:**
Every polynomial equation $P(x) = 0$ of any degree with complex number coefficients has at least one complex number solution.

**The Number of Roots of a Polynomial Equation Theorem:**
Every polynomial equation of degree $n$ has exactly $n$ roots, provided that multiple roots are counted as separate roots.

# Lesson 11-6: Example 3

$$x^5 - 7x^3 + 15x^2 + 3 = 10$$

| x | y |
|---|---|
| -50 | -311587507 |
| -40 | -101928007 |
| -30 | -24097507 |
| -20 | -3138007 |
| -10 | -91507 |
| 0 | -7 |
| 10 | 94493 |
| 20 | 3149993 |
| 30 | 24124493 |
| 40 | 101975993 |
| 50 | 311662493 |

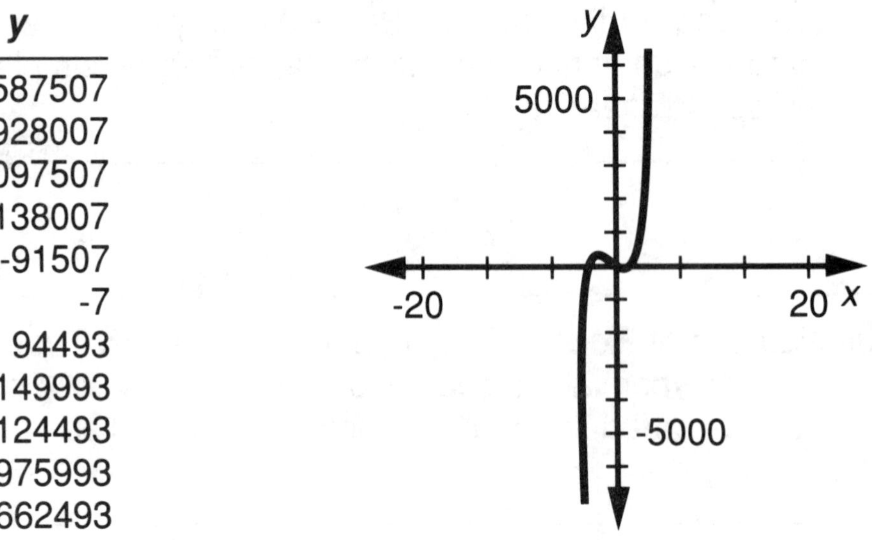


$$y = x^5 - 7x^3 + 15x^2 - 7$$

| x | y |
|---|---|
| -5 | -1882 |
| -4 | -343 |
| -3 | 74 |
| -2 | 77 |
| -1 | 14 |
| 0 | -7 |
| 1 | 2 |
| 2 | 29 |
| 3 | 182 |

# Lesson 11-7: Question 25

***Multiple choice***

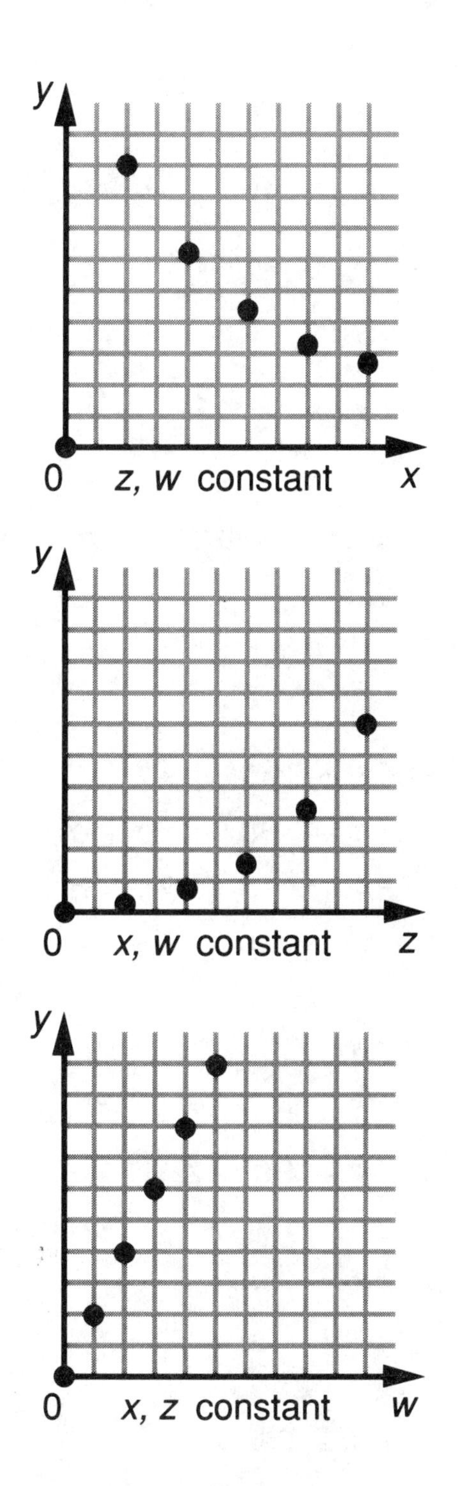


Which of the following equations could describe the relationships graphed above, where $k$ is a constant?

(a) $y = \frac{kwz}{x^2}$ (b) $y = kwzx$ (c) $y = \frac{kwx^2}{z}$ (d) $y = \frac{kwz^2}{x}$

# Lesson 11-8: Example 2

| **Number of Rows** | **1** | **2** | **3** | **4** | **5** | **6** | **...** |
|---|---|---|---|---|---|---|---|
| **Number of Oranges** | **1** | **5** | **14** | **30** | **55** | **91** | **...** |

1st Differences: 4 9 16 25 36 ...

2nd Differences: 5 7 9 11

3rd Differences: 2 2 2

$$\mathbf{f(n) = an^3 + bn^2 + cn + d}$$

$$\begin{cases} f(4) = 64a + 16b + 4c + d = 30 \\ f(3) = 27a + 9b + 3c + d = 14 \\ f(2) = 8a + 4b + 2c + d = 5 \\ f(1) = a + b + c + d = 1 \end{cases}$$

$$\begin{cases} 37a + 7b + c = 16 \\ 19a + 5b + c = 9 \\ 7a + 3b + c = 4 \end{cases}$$

$$\begin{cases} 18a + 2b = 7 \\ 12a + 2b = 5 \end{cases}$$

$$6a = 2$$

$$\mathbf{f(n) = \tfrac{1}{3}n^3 + \tfrac{1}{2}n^2 + \tfrac{1}{6}n}$$

# Conic Sections

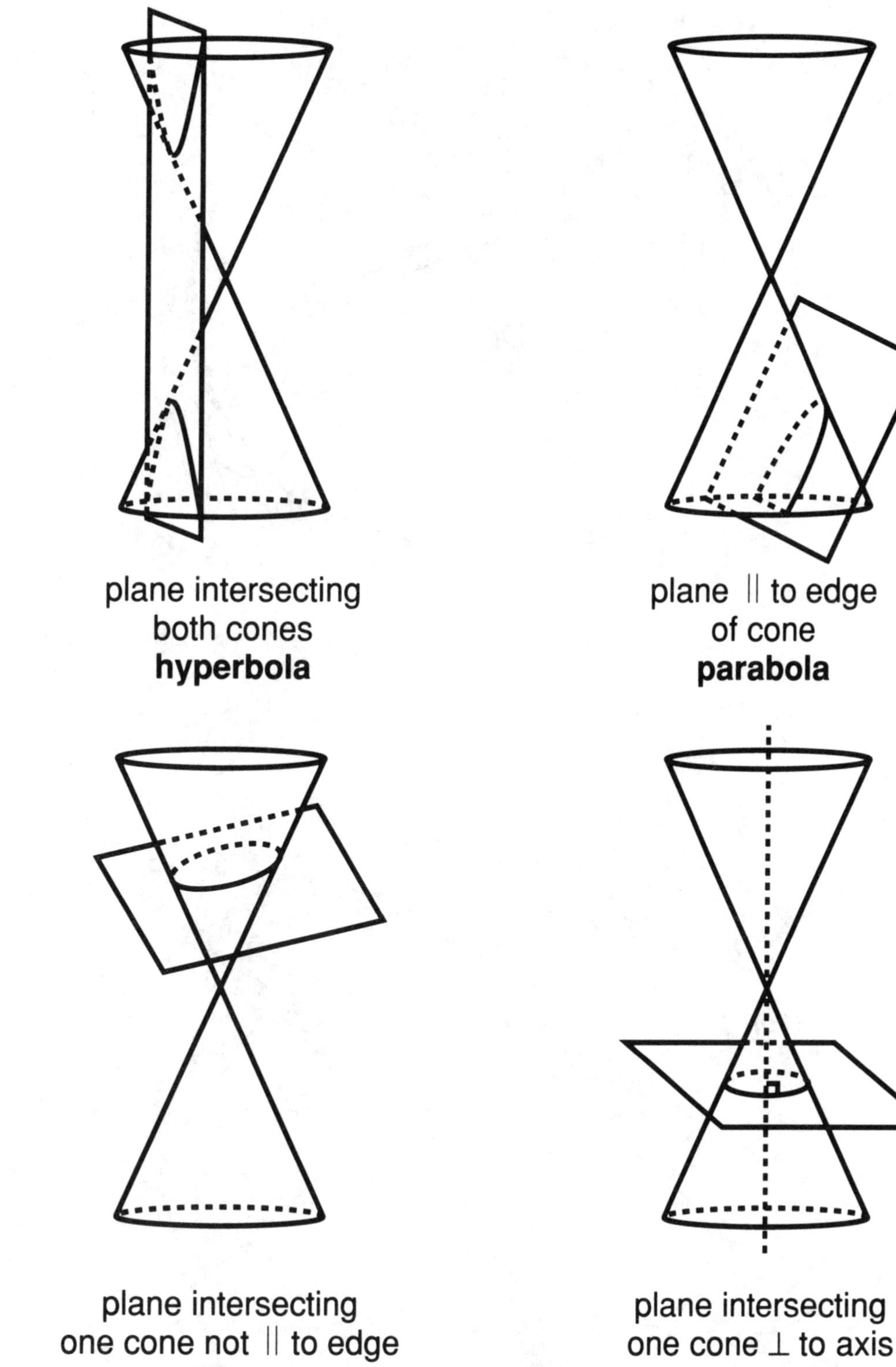

plane intersecting
both cones
**hyperbola**
plane $\parallel$ to edge
of cone
**parabola**
plane intersecting
one cone not $\parallel$ to edge
**ellipse**
plane intersecting
one cone $\perp$ to axis
**circle**

# Lessons 12-3: Examples 1 and 2

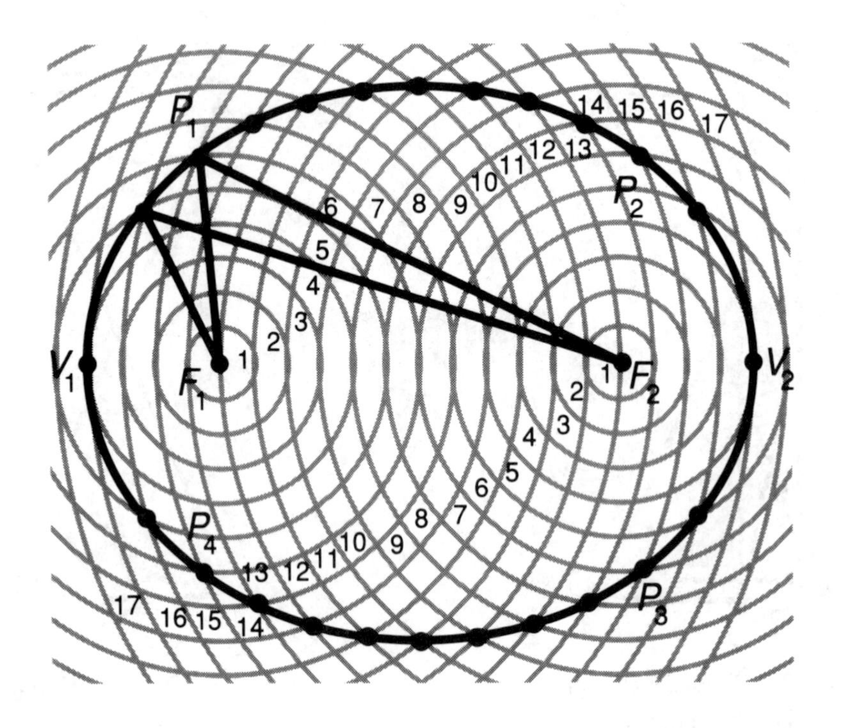


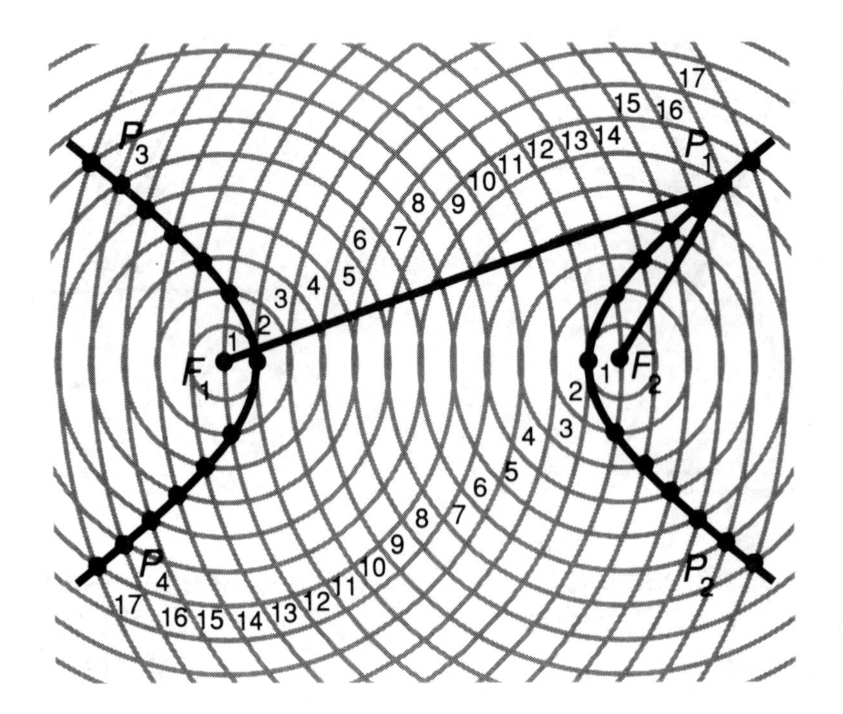

# Conic Graph Paper

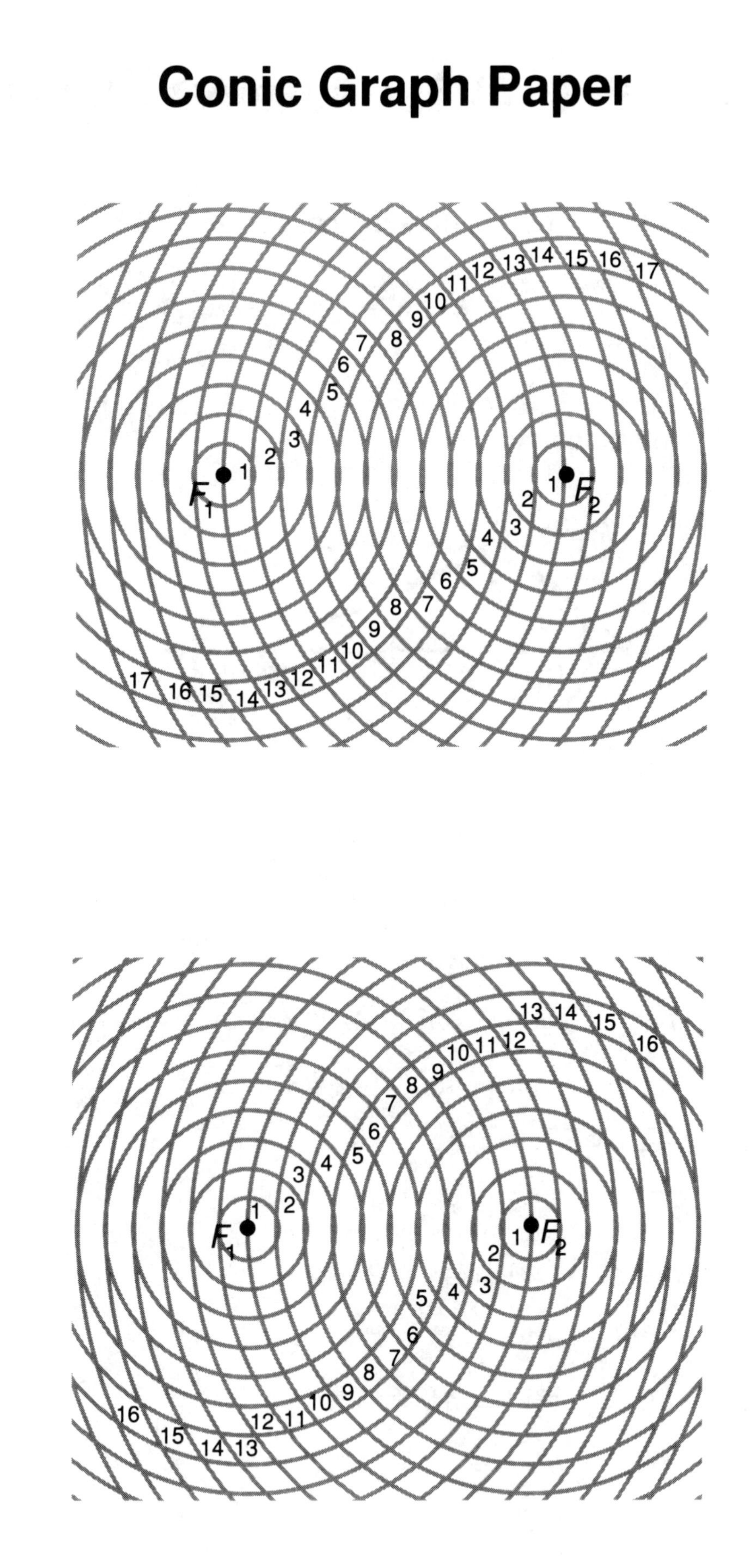

# Theorem (Equation for an Ellipse)

The ellipse with foci $(c, 0)$ and $(-c, 0)$ and focal constant $2a$ has equation

$$\frac{x^2}{a^2} + \frac{y^2}{b^2} = 1, \text{ where } b^2 = a^2 - c^2.$$

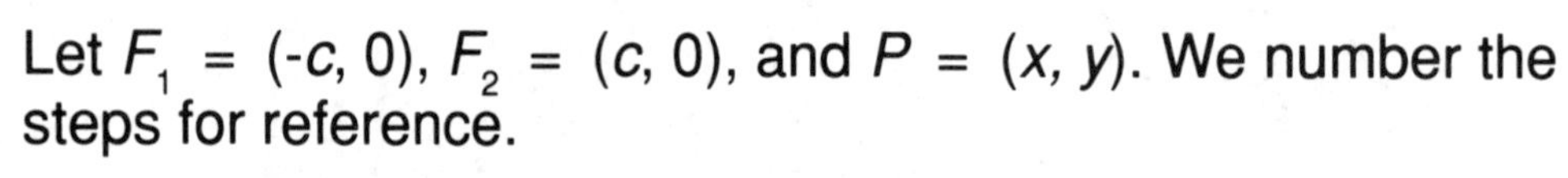

Proof Let $F_1 = (-c, 0)$, $F_2 = (c, 0)$, and $P = (x, y)$. We number the steps for reference.

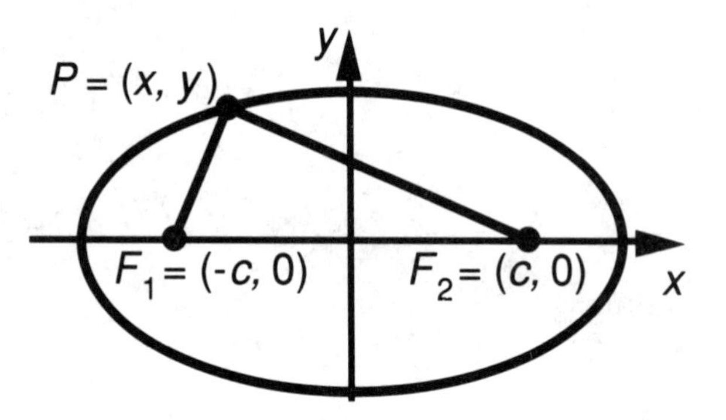


1. $$PF_1 + PF_2 = 2a$$

$$\sqrt{(x + c)^2 + y^2} + \sqrt{(x - c)^2 + y^2} = 2a$$

2. $$\sqrt{(x - c)^2 + y^2} = 2a - \sqrt{(x + c)^2 + y^2}$$

3. $$(x - c)^2 + y^2 = 4a^2 - 4a\sqrt{(x + c)^2 + y^2} + (x + c)^2 + y^2$$

4. $$-2cx = 4a^2 - 4a\sqrt{(x + c)^2 + y^2} + 2cx$$

5. $$4a\sqrt{(x + c)^2 + y^2} = 4a^2 + cx$$

6. $$a\sqrt{(x + c)^2 + y^2} = a^2 + cx$$

7. $$a^2[(x + c)^2 + y^2] = a^4 + 2a^2cx + c^2x^2$$

8. $$a^2x^2 + a^2c^2 + a^2y^2 = a^4 + c^2x^2$$

9. $$(a^2 - c^2)x^2 + a^2y^2 = a^2(a^2 - c^2)$$

10. $$b^2x^2 + a^2y^2 = a^2b^2$$

11. $$\frac{x^2}{a^2} + \frac{y^2}{b^2} = 1$$

# Lesson 12-6: Proof of a Theorem

**Theorem:**
The hyperbola with foci (6, 6) and (6, -6) and focal constant 12 has equation

$$y = \frac{18}{x}.$$

**Proof**

1. $PF_1 - PF_1 = d$

2. $\sqrt{(x-6)^2 + (y-6)^2} - \sqrt{(x+6)^2 + (y+6)^2} = 12$

3. $\sqrt{(x-6)^2 + (y-6)^2} = 12 + \sqrt{(x+6)^2 + (y+6)^2}$

4. $(x-6)^2 + (y-6)^2 =$

   $144 + 24\sqrt{(x+6)^2 + (y+6)^2} + (x+6)^2 + (y+6)^2$

5. $x^2 - 12x + 36 + y^2 - 12y + 36 =$

   $144 + 24\sqrt{(x+6)^2 + (y+6)^2} + x^2 + 12x + 36 + y^2 + 12y + 36$

6. $-24x - 24y - 144 = 24\sqrt{(x+6)^2 + (y+6)^2}$

7. $(x + y + 6)^2 = (x+6)^2 + (y+6)^2$

8. $x^2 + y^2 + 12x + 12y + 2xy + 36 = x^2 + 12x + 36 + y^2 + 12y + 36$

9. $2xy = 36$

10. $y = \frac{18}{x}$

# Lesson 12-8: Question 24

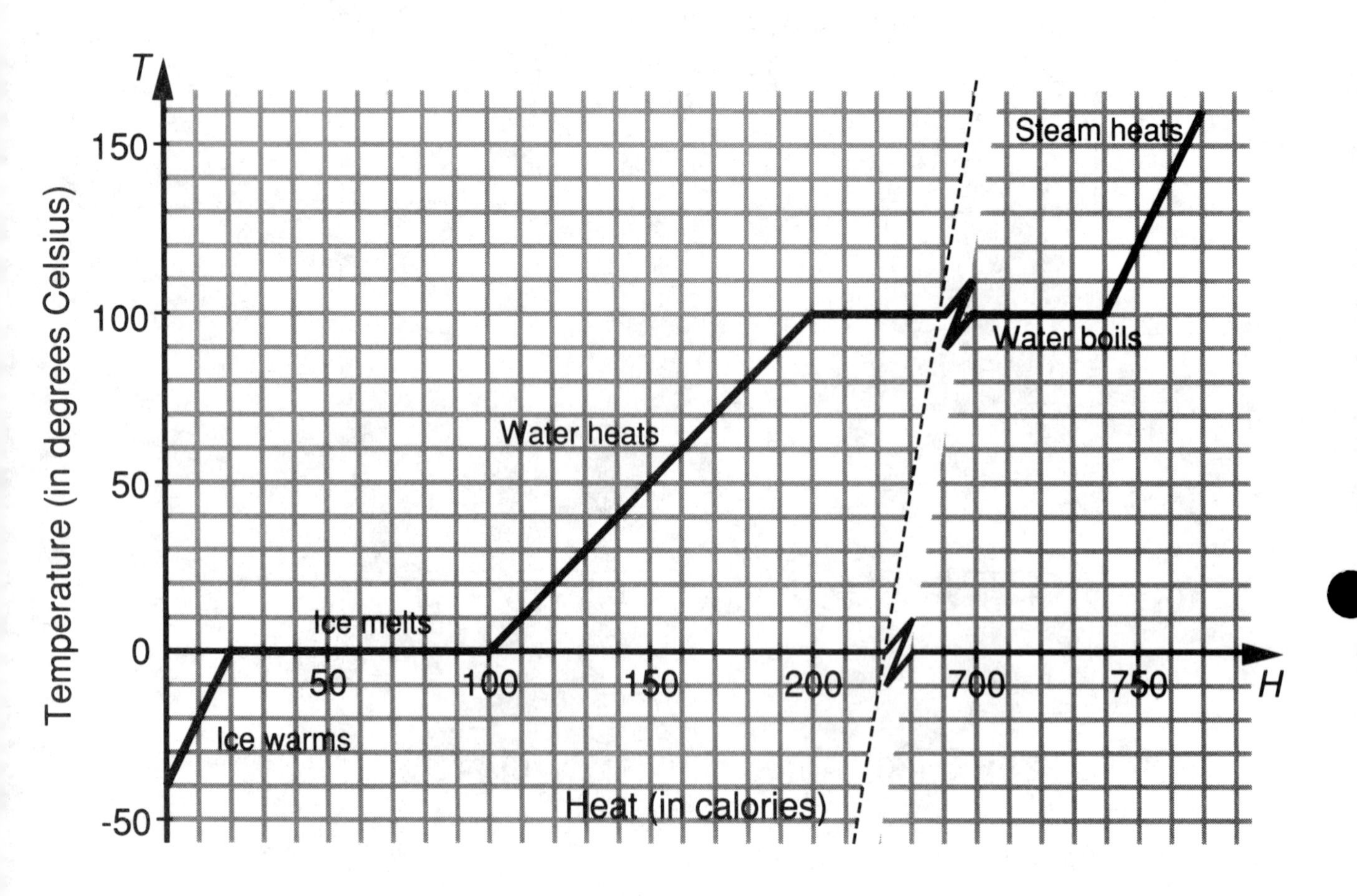

# Conic Sections in Standard Form

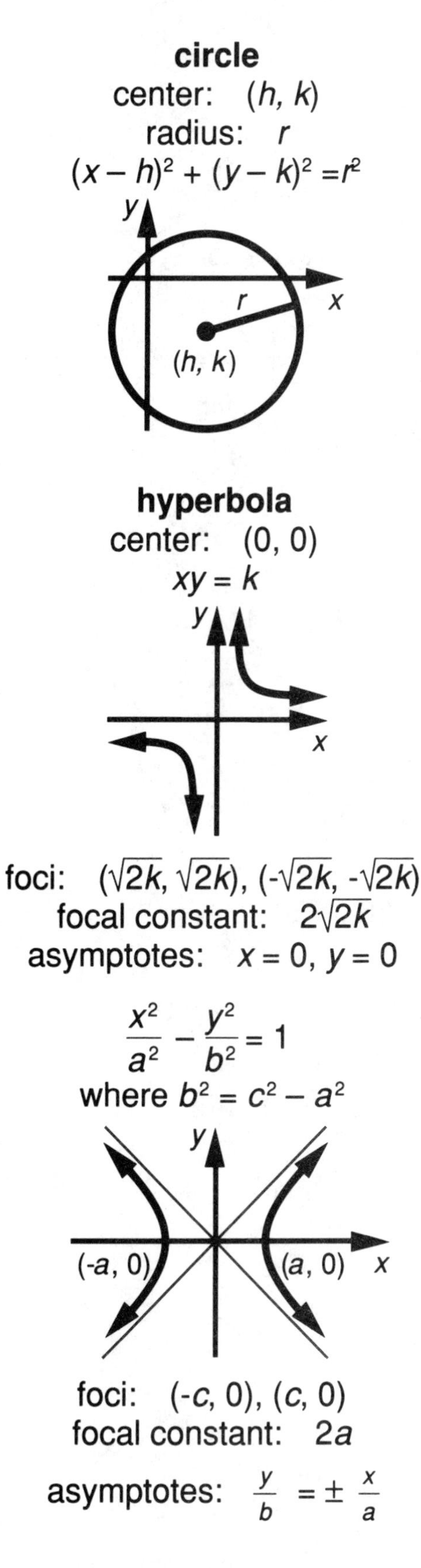


**circle**

center: $(h, k)$

radius: $r$

$(x - h)^2 + (y - k)^2 = r^2$

**hyperbola**

center: $(0, 0)$

$xy = k$

foci: $(\sqrt{2k}, \sqrt{2k}), (-\sqrt{2k}, -\sqrt{2k})$

focal constant: $2\sqrt{2k}$

asymptotes: $x = 0$, $y = 0$

$$\frac{x^2}{a^2} - \frac{y^2}{b^2} = 1$$

where $b^2 = c^2 - a^2$

foci: $(-c, 0), (c, 0)$

focal constant: $2a$

asymptotes: $\frac{y}{b} = \pm \frac{x}{a}$

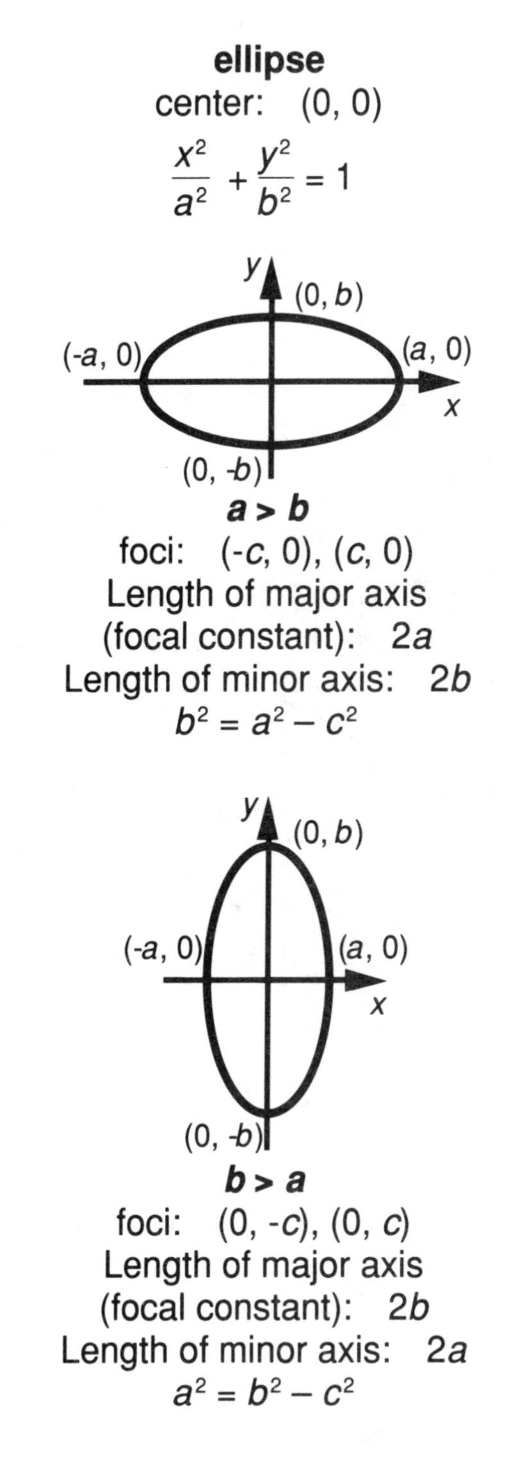


**ellipse**

center: $(0, 0)$

$$\frac{x^2}{a^2} + \frac{y^2}{b^2} = 1$$

***a* > *b***

foci: $(-c, 0), (c, 0)$

Length of major axis

(focal constant): $2a$

Length of minor axis: $2b$

$b^2 = a^2 - c^2$

***b* > *a***

foci: $(0, -c), (0, c)$

Length of major axis

(focal constant): $2b$

Length of minor axis: $2a$

$a^2 = b^2 - c^2$

# Pascal's Triangle

| | | | | | | | | | | | | | | | | | | | | | |
|---|---|---|---|---|---|---|---|---|---|---|---|---|---|---|---|---|---|---|---|---|---|
| row 0 → | | | | | | | | | | | 1 | | | | | | | | | | |
| row 1 → | | | | | | | | | | 1 | | 1 | | | | | | | | | |
| row 2 → | | | | | | | | | 1 | | 2 | | 1 | | | | | | | | |
| row 3 → | | | | | | | | 1 | | 3 | | 3 | | 1 | | | | | | | |
| row 4 → | | | | | | | 1 | | 4 | | 6 | | 4 | | 1 | | | | | | |
| row 5 → | | | | | | 1 | | 5 | | 10 | | 10 | | 5 | | 1 | | | | | |
| row 6 → | | | | | 1 | | 6 | | 15 | | 20 | | 15 | | 6 | | 1 | | | | |
| row 7 → | | | | 1 | | 7 | | 21 | | 35 | | 35 | | 21 | | 7 | | 1 | | | |
| row 8 → | | | 1 | | 8 | | 28 | | 56 | | 70 | | 56 | | 28 | | 8 | | 1 | | |
| row 9 → | | 1 | | 9 | | 36 | | 84 | | 126 | | 126 | | 84 | | 36 | | 9 | | 1 | |
| row 10 → | 1 | | 10 | | 45 | | 120 | | 210 | | 252 | | 210 | | 120 | | 45 | | 10 | | 1 |

# Binomial Theorem

$$(a + b)^n = \sum_{r=0}^{n} \binom{n}{r} a^{n-r} b^r$$

$$(a + b)^0 = \binom{0}{0}$$

$$(a + b)^1 = \binom{1}{0}a + \binom{1}{1}b$$

$$(a + b)^2 = \binom{2}{0}a^2 + \binom{2}{1}ab + \binom{2}{2}b^2$$

$$(a + b)^3 = \binom{3}{0}a^3 + \binom{3}{1}a^2b + \binom{3}{2}ab^2 + \binom{3}{3}b^3$$

$$(a + b)^4 = \binom{4}{0}a^4 + \binom{4}{1}a^3b + \binom{4}{2}a^2b^2 + \binom{4}{3}ab^3 + \binom{4}{4}b^4$$

# Lesson 13-8: Example 1

| | | | |
|---|---|---|---|
| RRRRR | RWRRR | WRRRR | WWRRR |
| RRRRW | RWRRW | WRRRW | WWRRW |
| RRRWR | RWRWR | WRRWR | WWRWR |
| RRRWW | RWRWW | WRRWW | WWRWW |
| RRWRR | RWWRR | WRWRR | WWWRR |
| RRWRW | RWWRW | WRWRW | WWWRW |
| RRWWR | RWWWR | WRWWR | WWWWR |
| RRWWW | RWWWW | WRWWW | WWWWW |

# Lesson 13-9: Definitions

Let $S$ be a data set of $n$ numbers $\{S_1, S_2, S_3, \ldots, S_n\}$.

mean of $S$ = the *average* of all terms of $S = \dfrac{\sum_{i=1}^{n} S_i}{n}$.

median of $S$ = the *middle* term of $S$ when the terms are placed in increasing order.

mode of $S$ = the number which occurs most often in the sequence.

Let $S$ be a data set of $n$ numbers $\{S_1, S_2, \ldots, S_n\}$. Let $m$ be the mean of $S$. Then the standard deviation s.d. of $S$ is

$$\text{s.d.} = \sqrt{\dfrac{\sum_{i=1}^{n} (S_i - m)^2}{n}}.$$

# Binomial and Normal Distributions for 10 Tosses of a Fair Coin

### Binomial Distribution

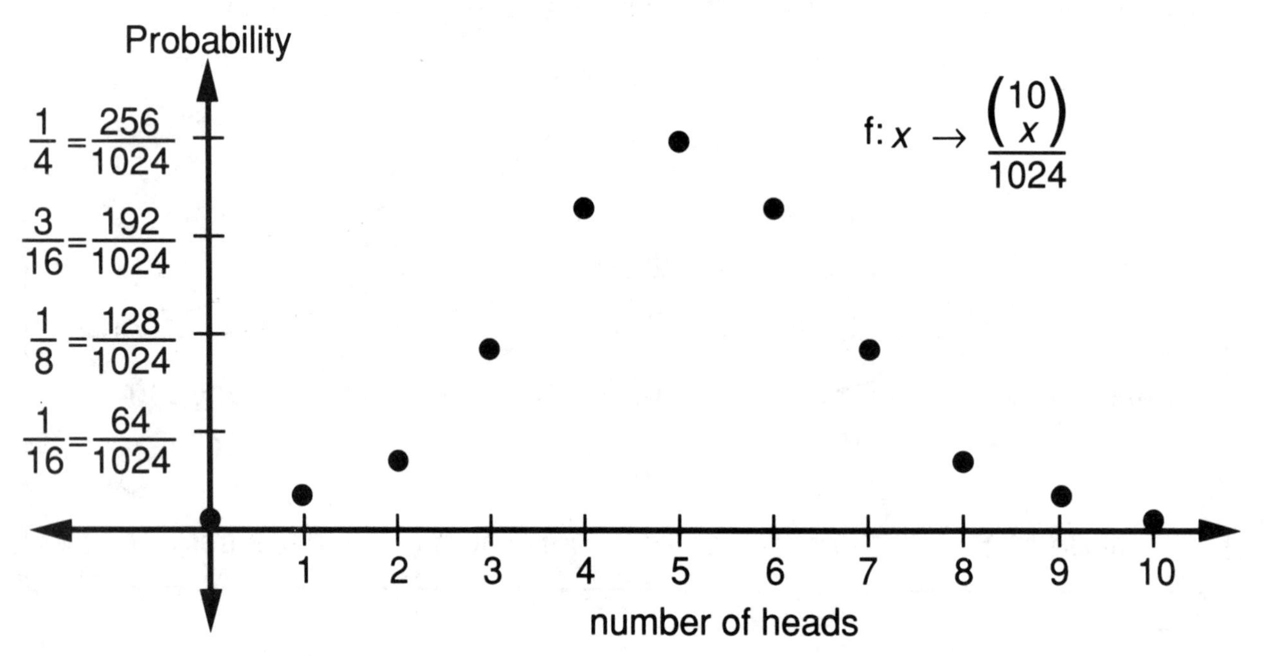


### Normal Distribution

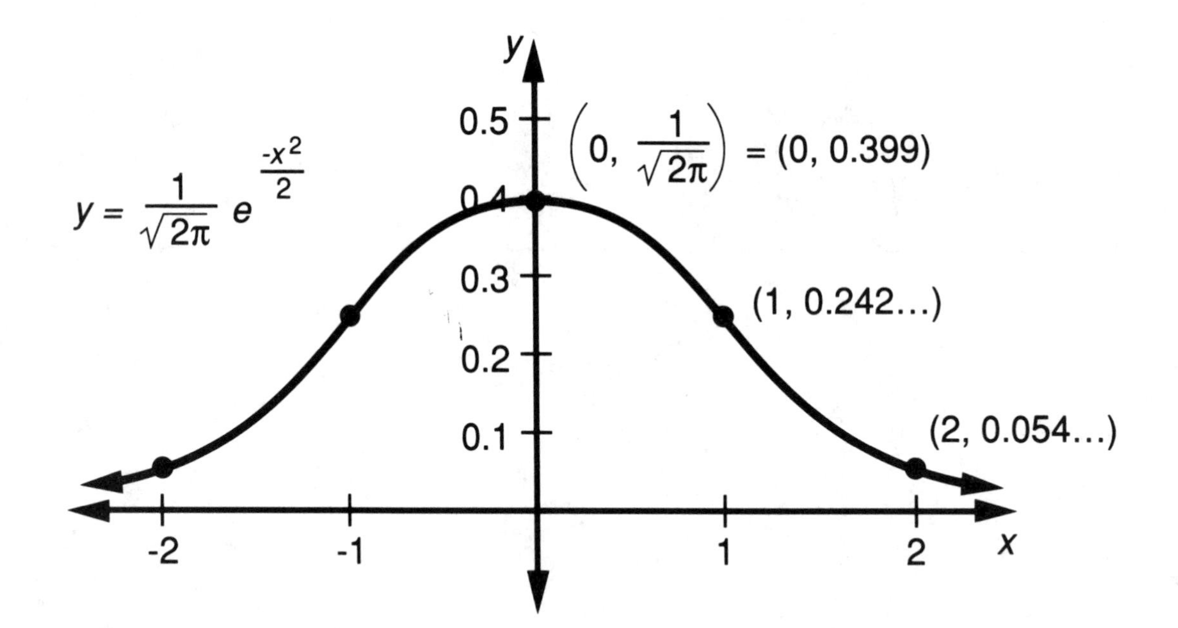

# Standardized SAT and IQ Scores

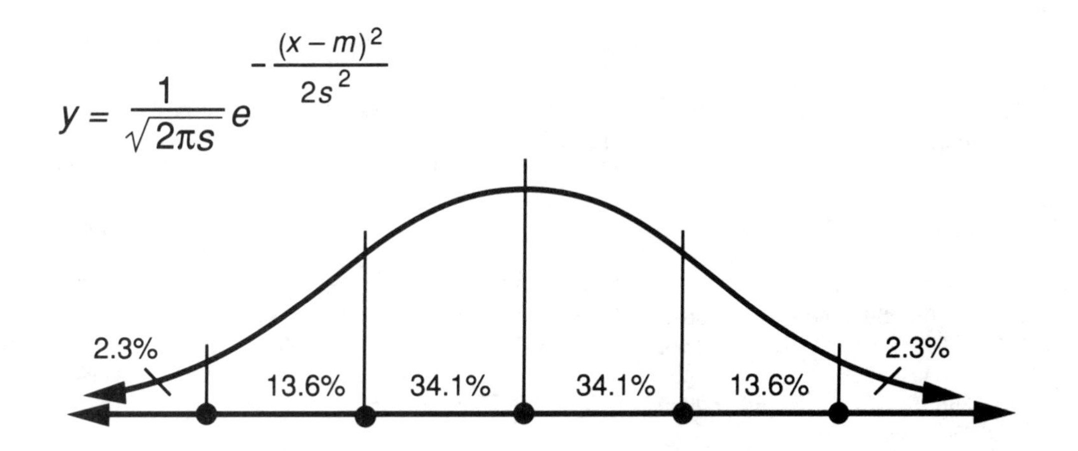


| | | | | | | |
|---|---|---|---|---|---|---|
| General application | → | $m - 2s$ | $m - s$ | $m$ | $m + s$ | $m + 2s$ |
| Normal curve | → | -2 | -1 | 0 | 1 | 2 |
| SATs | → | 300 | 400 | 500 | 600 | 700 |
| IQ test | → | 70 | 85 | 100 | 115 | 130 |

# Random Number Table

| col. row | 1 | 2 | 3 | 4 | 5 | 6 | 7 | 8 | 9 | 10 | 11 | 12 | 13 | 14 |
|---|---|---|---|---|---|---|---|---|---|---|---|---|---|---|
| 1 | 10480 | 15011 | 01536 | 02011 | 81647 | 91646 | 69719 | 14194 | 62590 | 36207 | 20969 | 99570 | 91291 | 90700 |
| 2 | 22368 | 46573 | 25595 | 85393 | 30995 | 89198 | 27982 | 53402 | 93965 | 34095 | 52666 | 19174 | 39615 | 99505 |
| 3 | 24130 | 48360 | 22527 | 97265 | 76393 | 64809 | 15179 | 24830 | 49340 | 32081 | 30680 | 19655 | 63348 | 58629 |
| 4 | 42167 | 93093 | 06423 | 61680 | 17856 | 16376 | 39440 | 53537 | 71341 | 57004 | 00849 | 74917 | 97758 | 16379 |
| 5 | 37570 | 39975 | 81837 | 16656 | 06121 | 91782 | 60468 | 81305 | 49684 | 60672 | 14110 | 06927 | 01263 | 54613 |
| 6 | 77921 | 06907 | 11008 | 42751 | 27756 | 53498 | 18602 | 70659 | 90655 | 15053 | 21916 | 81825 | 44394 | 42880 |
| 7 | 99562 | 72905 | 56420 | 69994 | 98872 | 31016 | 71194 | 18738 | 44013 | 48840 | 63213 | 21069 | 10634 | 12952 |
| 8 | 96301 | 91977 | 05463 | 07972 | 18876 | 20922 | 94595 | 56869 | 69014 | 60045 | 18425 | 84903 | 42508 | 32307 |
| 9 | 89579 | 14342 | 63661 | 10281 | 17453 | 18103 | 57740 | 84378 | 25331 | 12566 | 58678 | 44947 | 05585 | 56941 |
| 10 | 85475 | 36857 | 43342 | 53988 | 53060 | 59533 | 38867 | 62300 | 08158 | 17983 | 16439 | 11458 | 18593 | 64952 |
| 11 | 28918 | 69578 | 88231 | 33276 | 70997 | 79936 | 56865 | 05859 | 90106 | 31595 | 01547 | 85590 | 91610 | 78188 |
| 12 | 63553 | 40961 | 48235 | 03427 | 49626 | 69445 | 18663 | 72695 | 52180 | 20847 | 12234 | 90511 | 33703 | 90322 |
| 13 | 09429 | 93969 | 52636 | 92737 | 88974 | 33488 | 36320 | 17617 | 30015 | 08272 | 84115 | 27156 | 30613 | 74952 |
| 14 | 10365 | 61129 | 87529 | 85689 | 48237 | 52267 | 67689 | 93394 | 01511 | 26358 | 85104 | 20285 | 29975 | 89868 |
| 15 | 07119 | 97336 | 71048 | 08178 | 77233 | 13916 | 47564 | 81056 | 97735 | 85977 | 29372 | 74461 | 28551 | 90707 |
| 16 | 51085 | 12765 | 51821 | 51259 | 77452 | 16308 | 60756 | 92144 | 49442 | 53900 | 70960 | 63990 | 75601 | 40719 |
| 17 | 02368 | 21382 | 52404 | 60268 | 89368 | 19885 | 55322 | 44819 | 01188 | 65255 | 64835 | 44919 | 05944 | 55157 |
| 18 | 01011 | 54092 | 33362 | 94904 | 31272 | 04146 | 18594 | 29852 | 71585 | 85030 | 51132 | 01915 | 92747 | 64951 |
| 19 | 52162 | 53916 | 46369 | 58586 | 23216 | 14513 | 83149 | 98736 | 23495 | 64350 | 94738 | 17752 | 35156 | 35749 |
| 20 | 07056 | 97628 | 33787 | 09998 | 42698 | 06691 | 76988 | 13602 | 51851 | 46104 | 88916 | 19509 | 25625 | 58104 |
| 21 | 48663 | 91245 | 85828 | 14346 | 09172 | 30168 | 90229 | 04734 | 59193 | 22178 | 30421 | 61666 | 99904 | 32812 |
| 22 | 54164 | 58492 | 22421 | 74103 | 47070 | 25306 | 76468 | 26384 | 58151 | 06646 | 21524 | 15227 | 96909 | 44592 |
| 23 | 32639 | 32363 | 05597 | 24200 | 13363 | 38005 | 94342 | 28728 | 35806 | 06912 | 17012 | 64161 | 18296 | 22851 |
| 24 | 29334 | 27001 | 87637 | 87308 | 58731 | 00256 | 45834 | 15398 | 46557 | 41135 | 10367 | 07684 | 36188 | 18510 |
| 25 | 02488 | 33062 | 28834 | 07351 | 19731 | 92420 | 60952 | 61280 | 50001 | 67658 | 32586 | 86679 | 50720 | 94953 |
| 26 | 81525 | 72295 | 04839 | 96423 | 24878 | 82651 | 66566 | 14778 | 76797 | 14780 | 13300 | 87074 | 79666 | 95725 |
| 27 | 29676 | 20591 | 68086 | 26432 | 46901 | 20849 | 89768 | 81536 | 86645 | 12659 | 92259 | 57102 | 80428 | 25280 |
| 28 | 00742 | 57392 | 39064 | 66432 | 84673 | 40027 | 32832 | 61362 | 98947 | 96067 | 64760 | 64584 | 96096 | 98253 |
| 29 | 05366 | 04213 | 25669 | 26422 | 44407 | 44048 | 37937 | 63904 | 45766 | 66134 | 75470 | 66520 | 34693 | 90449 |
| 30 | 91921 | 26418 | 64117 | 94305 | 26766 | 25940 | 39972 | 22209 | 71500 | 64568 | 91402 | 42416 | 07844 | 69618 |
| 31 | 00582 | 04711 | 87917 | 77341 | 42206 | 35126 | 74087 | 99547 | 81817 | 42607 | 43808 | 76655 | 62028 | 76630 |
| 32 | 00725 | 69884 | 62797 | 56170 | 86324 | 88072 | 76222 | 36086 | 84637 | 93161 | 76038 | 65855 | 77919 | 88006 |
| 33 | 69011 | 65797 | 95876 | 55293 | 18988 | 27354 | 26575 | 08625 | 40801 | 59920 | 29841 | 80150 | 12777 | 48501 |
| 34 | 25976 | 57948 | 29888 | 88604 | 67917 | 48708 | 18912 | 82271 | 65424 | 69774 | 33611 | 54262 | 85963 | 03547 |
| 35 | 09763 | 83473 | 73577 | 12908 | 30883 | 18317 | 28290 | 35797 | 05998 | 41688 | 34952 | 37888 | 38917 | 88050 |
| 36 | 91567 | 42595 | 27958 | 30134 | 04024 | 86385 | 29880 | 99730 | 55536 | 84855 | 29080 | 09250 | 79656 | 73211 |
| 37 | 17955 | 56349 | 90999 | 49127 | 20044 | 59931 | 06115 | 20542 | 18059 | 02008 | 73708 | 83517 | 36103 | 42791 |
| 38 | 46503 | 18584 | 18845 | 49618 | 02304 | 51038 | 20655 | 58727 | 28168 | 15475 | 56942 | 53389 | 20562 | 87338 |
| 39 | 92157 | 89634 | 94824 | 78171 | 84610 | 82834 | 09922 | 25417 | 44137 | 48413 | 25555 | 21246 | 35509 | 20468 |
| 40 | 14577 | 62765 | 35605 | 81263 | 39667 | 47358 | 56873 | 56307 | 61607 | 49518 | 89656 | 20103 | 77490 | 18062 |

# Summary of Theorems

| |
|---|
| The sum of integers from 1 to $n$ is $\frac{1}{2}n(n+1)$. |
| Let $S_n = a_1 + a_2 + \ldots + a_n$ be an arithmetic series with constant difference $d$. Then, the value $S_n$ of that series is $S_n = \frac{n}{2}(a_1 + a_n)$ or $S_n = \frac{n}{2}[2a_1 + (n-1)d]$. |
| Let $g + gr + gr^2 + \ldots gr^{n-1}$ be the geometric series with $r \neq 1$. Then the value $S_n$ of that series is $S_n = \frac{g(1-r^n)}{1-r}$. |
| There are $n!$ permutations of $n$ distinct objects. |
| If $\lvert r \rvert < 1$, the infinite geometric series with first term $a$ and ratio $r$ has the value $S = \frac{g}{1-r}$. |
| $\binom{n}{r} = \frac{n!}{r!(n-r)!}$ |
| **Binomial Theorem:** $(a+b)^n = \sum_{r=0}^{n} \binom{n}{r} a^{n-r}b^r$. |
| The number of subsets of $r$ elements which can be formed from a set of $n$ elements is $\frac{n!}{r!(n-r)!}$, the biniomial coefficient $\binom{n}{r}$. |
| A set with $n$ elements has $2^n$ subsets. |
| If a situation consists of $n$ trials with the same two equally likely outcomes for each trial, then the probability of one of these outcomes occurring exactly $r$ times is $\frac{\binom{n}{r}}{2^n}$ |
| **Central Limit Theorem:** Suppose random samples of size $n$ are chosen from a population of events in which the probability of an event having certain characteristics is $p$. Let P($x$) equal the number of elements in that sample with the characteristic. Then P is approximated by a normal distribution with mean $np$ and standard deviation $\sqrt{np(1-p)}$. |

# 3-Dimensional Coordinate System

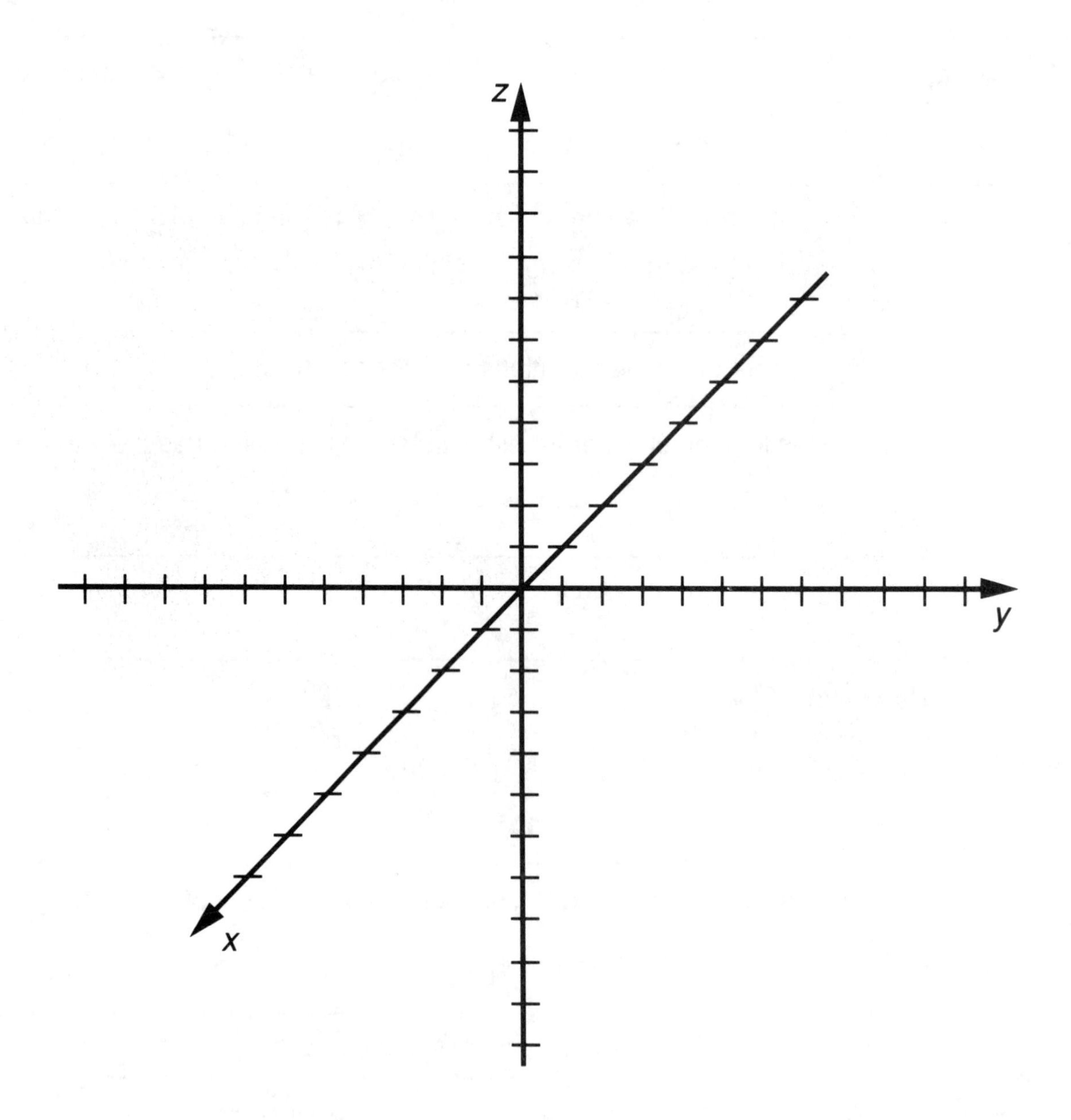

# Octants in 3-Space

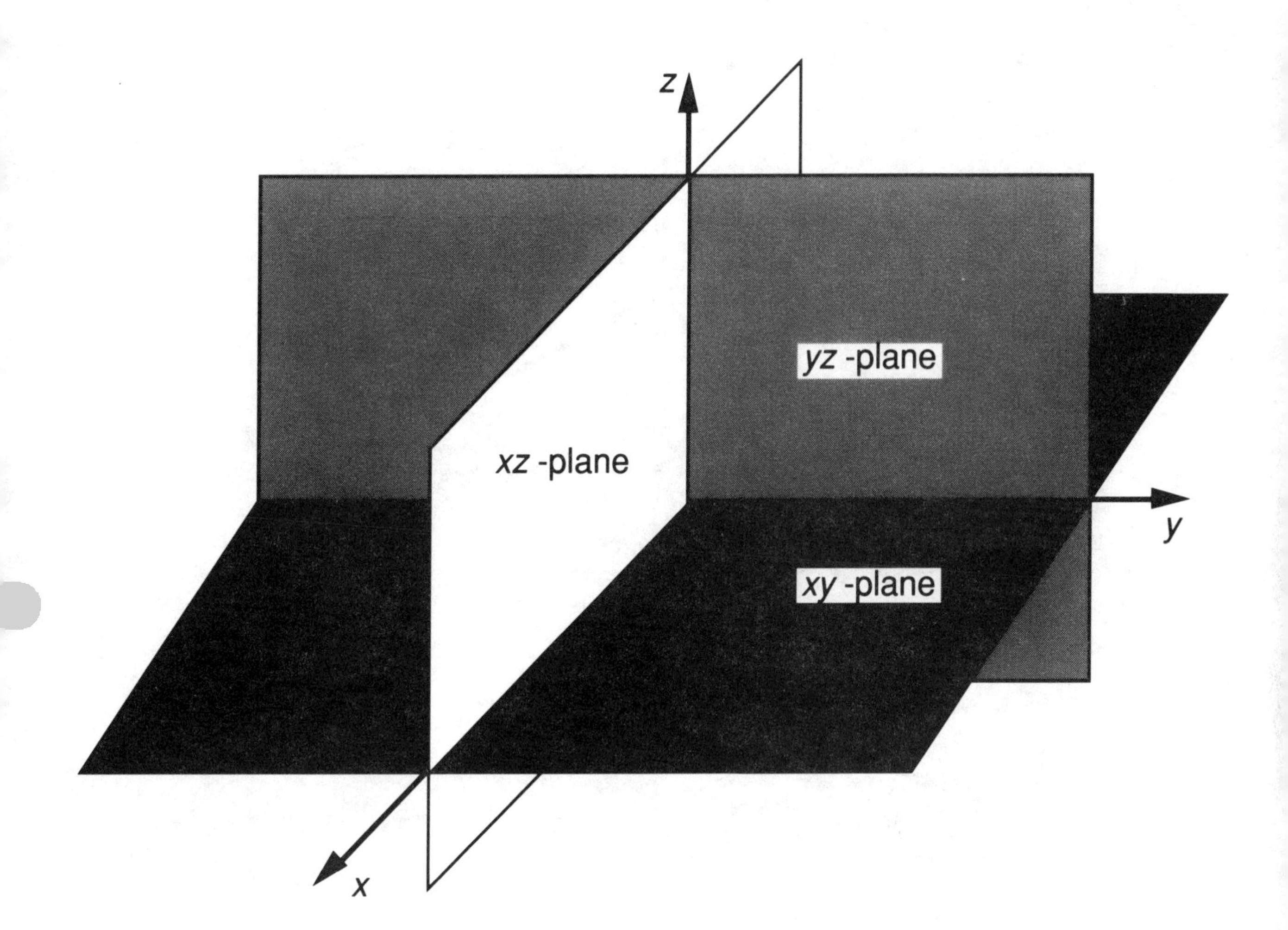

# Lesson 14-2: Example 2

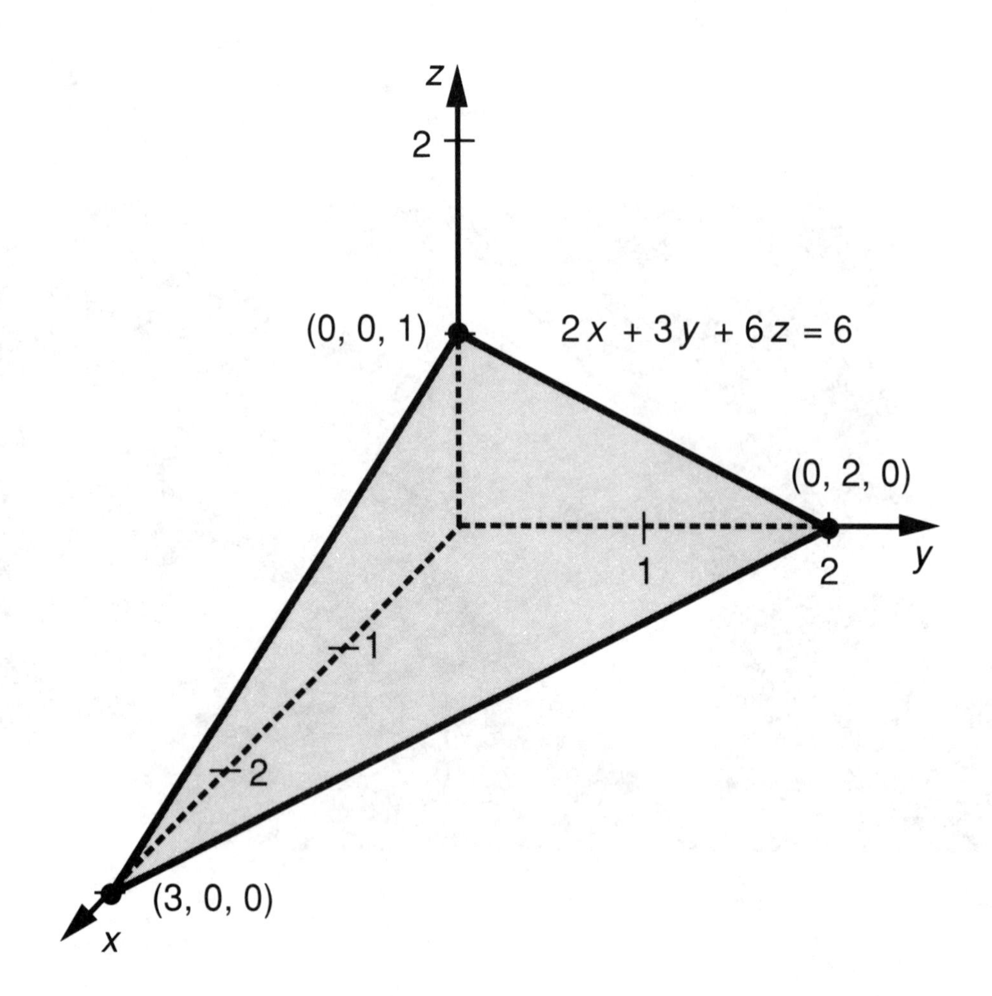

# 3 Planes Intersecting in a Point

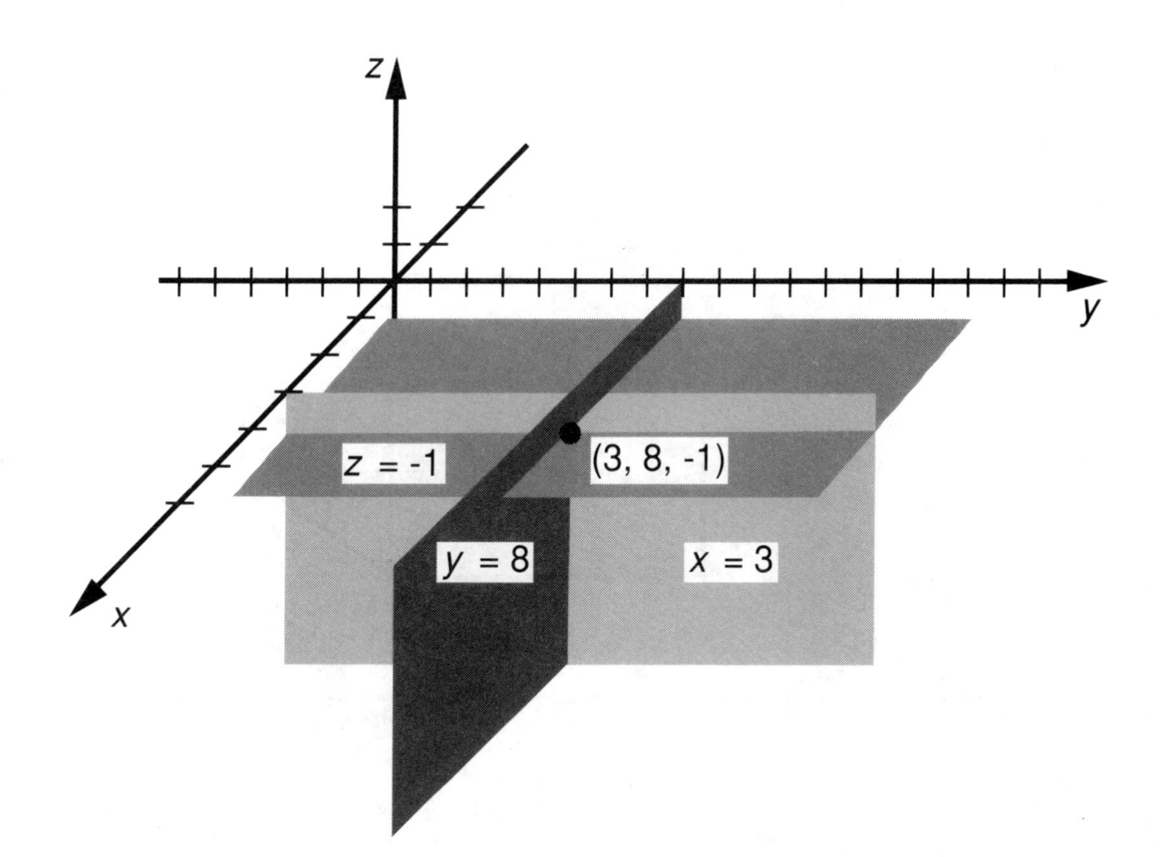

# The Distance Formula for 3-Space

The distance $d$ between points $(x_1, y_1, z_1)$ and $(x_2, y_2, z_2)$ is

$$d = \sqrt{(x_1 - x_2)^2 + (y_1 - y_2)^2 + (z_1 - z_2)^2}.$$

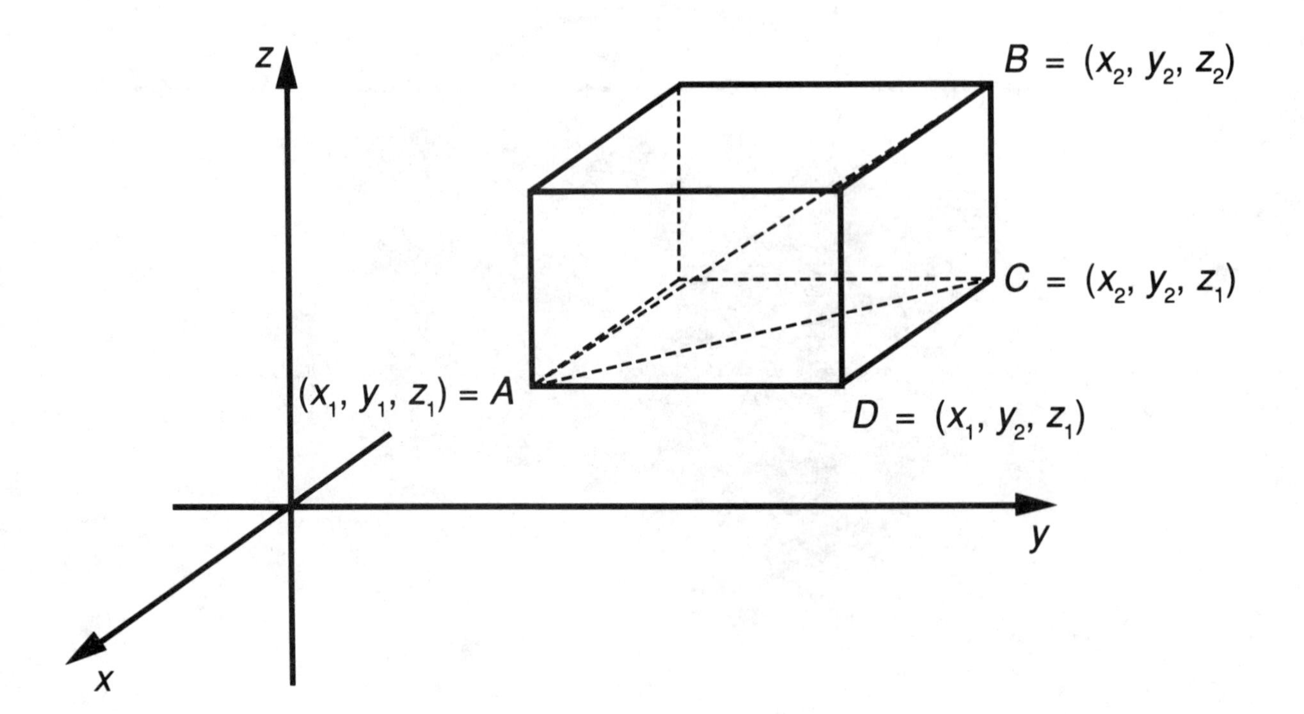

# Lesson 14-4: Example 3

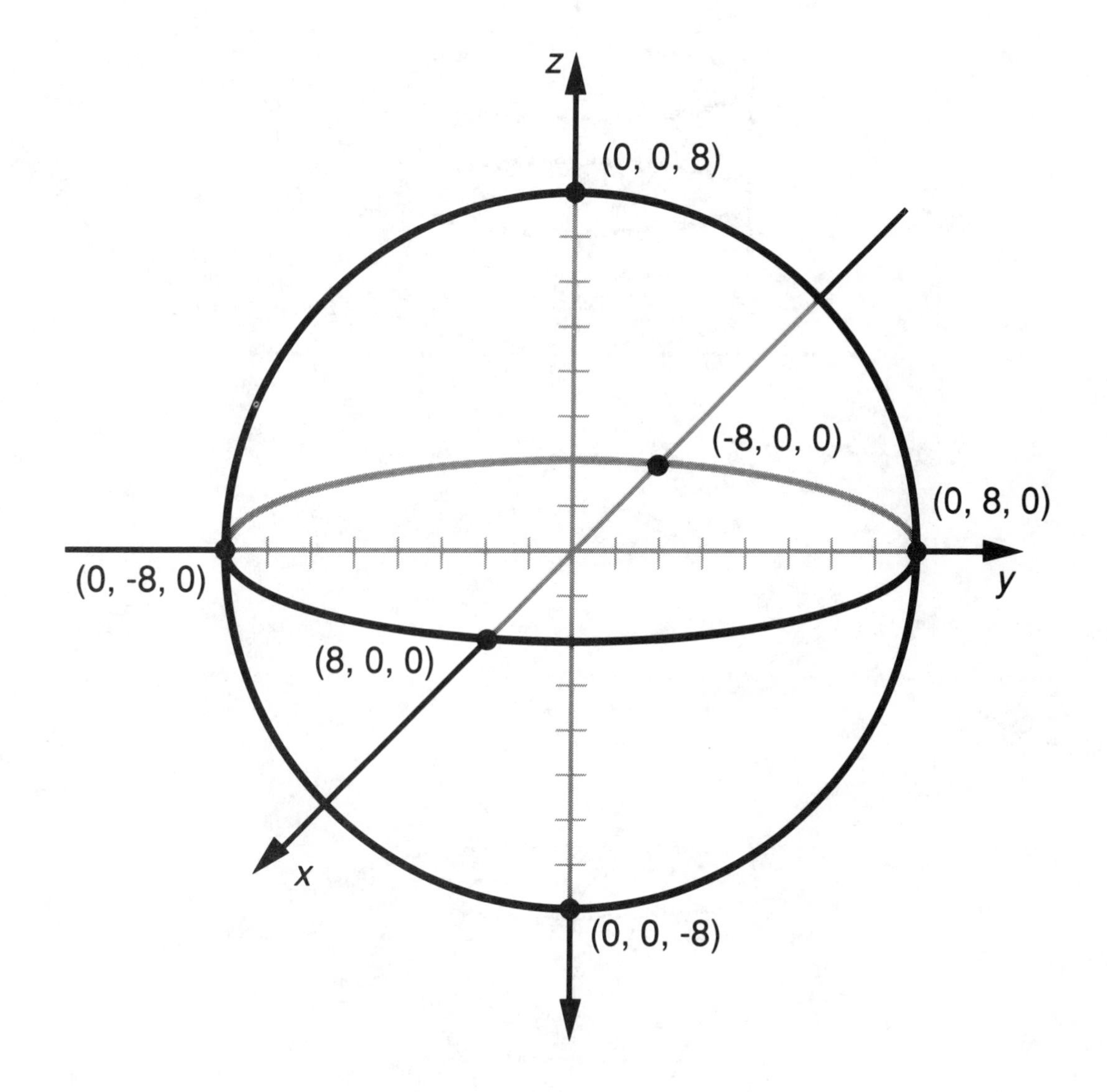

# Lesson 14-5: Examples

**Example 1**

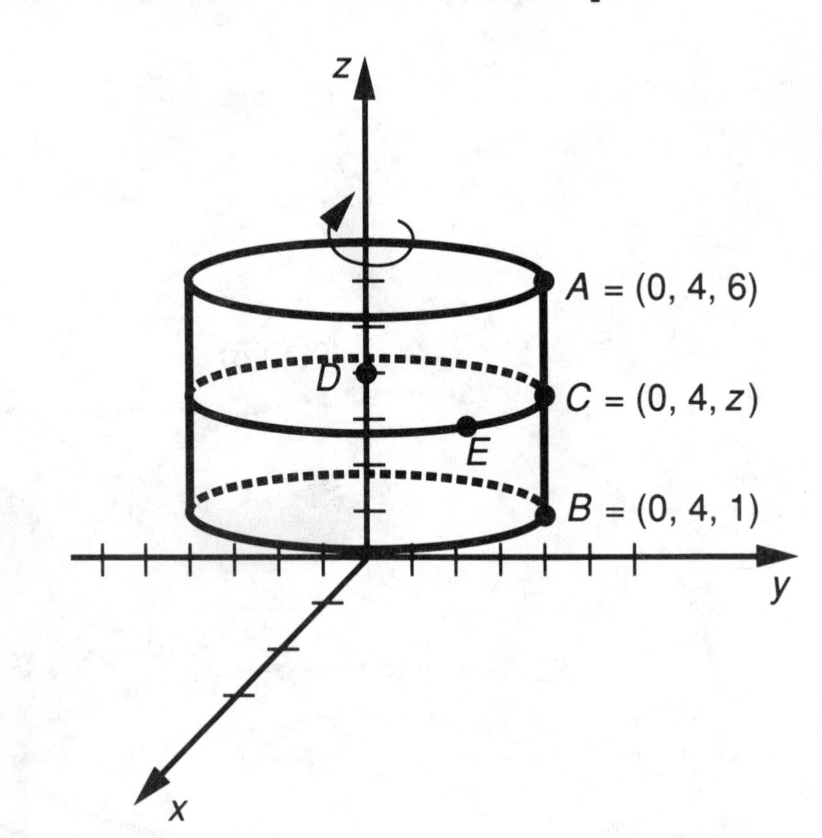


**Example 2**

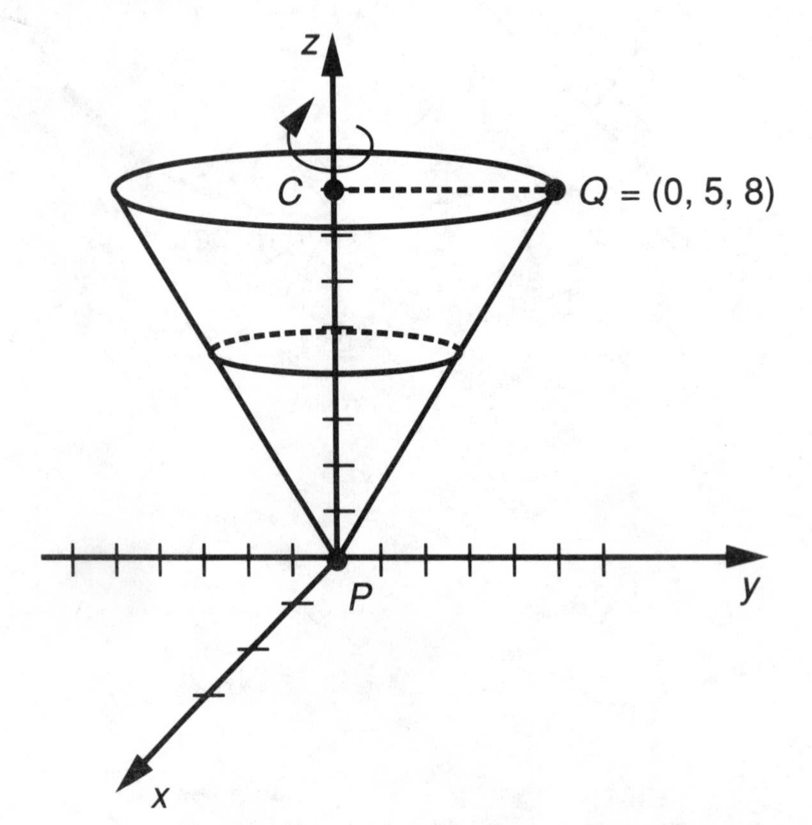

# The Four-Dimensional Hypercube

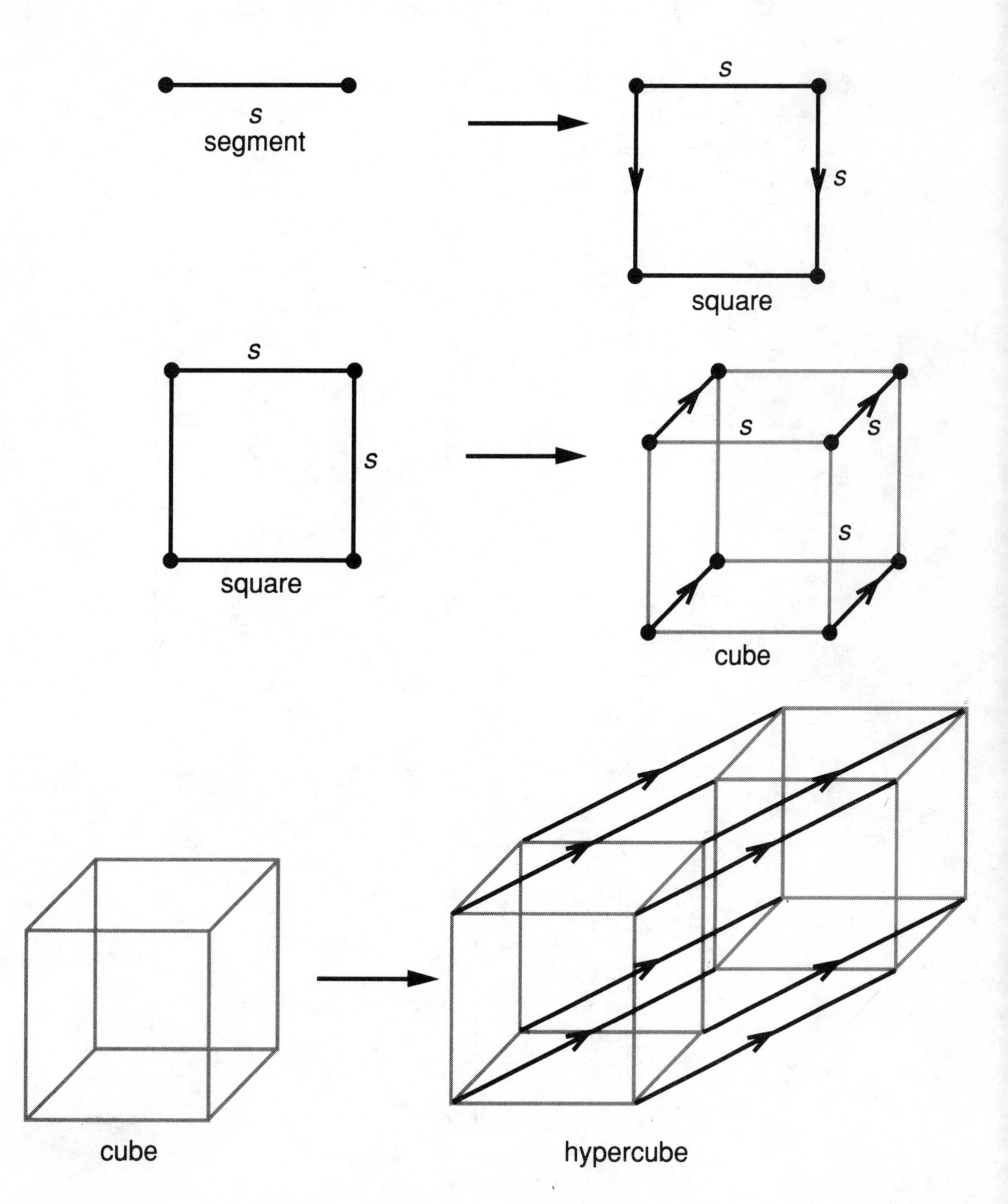

# Solving a System Using Augmented Matrices

$$\begin{cases} 5a + 4b + 8c - 2d = 28 \\ -3a - 4b + 2c + 3d = 16 \\ a + b + c = 4 \\ 2a + 3b - 2c + 5d = 1 \end{cases} \qquad \begin{bmatrix} 5 & 4 & 8 & -2 & 28 \\ -3 & -4 & 2 & 3 & 16 \\ 1 & 1 & 1 & 0 & 4 \\ 2 & 3 & -2 & 5 & 1 \end{bmatrix}$$

$$\begin{matrix} \text{(R1):} \\ \text{(R2):} \\ \text{(R3):} \\ \text{(R4):} \end{matrix} \quad \begin{bmatrix} 1 & 1 & 1 & 0 & 4 \\ -3 & -4 & 2 & 3 & 16 \\ 5 & 4 & 8 & -2 & 28 \\ 2 & 3 & -2 & 5 & 1 \end{bmatrix}$$

$$\begin{matrix} \\ 3 \cdot \text{(R1)} + \text{(R2):} \\ \\ \\ \end{matrix} \quad \begin{bmatrix} 1 & 1 & 1 & 0 & 4 \\ 0 & -1 & 5 & 3 & 28 \\ 5 & 4 & 8 & -2 & 28 \\ 2 & 3 & -2 & 5 & 1 \end{bmatrix}$$

$$\begin{matrix} \\ \\ -5 \cdot \text{(R1)} + \text{(R3):} \\ -2 \cdot \text{(R1)} + \text{(R4):} \end{matrix} \quad \begin{bmatrix} 1 & 1 & 1 & 0 & 4 \\ 0 & -1 & 5 & 3 & 28 \\ 0 & -1 & 3 & -2 & 8 \\ 0 & 1 & -4 & 5 & -7 \end{bmatrix}$$

$$\begin{matrix} \text{(R1):} \\ \text{(R2):} \\ \text{(R3):} \\ \text{(R4):} \end{matrix} \quad \begin{bmatrix} 1 & 1 & 1 & 0 & 4 \\ 0 & 1 & -4 & 5 & -7 \\ 0 & -1 & 3 & -2 & 8 \\ 0 & -1 & 5 & 3 & 28 \end{bmatrix}$$

$$\begin{matrix} \\ \\ \text{(R2)} + \text{(R3):} \\ \text{(R2)} + \text{(R4):} \end{matrix} \quad \begin{bmatrix} 1 & 1 & 1 & 0 & 4 \\ 0 & 1 & -4 & 5 & -7 \\ 0 & 0 & -1 & 3 & 1 \\ 0 & 0 & 1 & 8 & 21 \end{bmatrix}$$

$$\begin{matrix} \text{(R1):} \\ \text{(R2):} \\ \text{(R3):} \\ \text{(R4):} \end{matrix} \quad \begin{bmatrix} 1 & 1 & 1 & 0 & 4 \\ 0 & 1 & -4 & 5 & -7 \\ 0 & 0 & 1 & 8 & 21 \\ 0 & 0 & -1 & 3 & 1 \end{bmatrix}$$

$$\begin{matrix} \\ \\ \\ \text{(R3)} + \text{(R4):} \end{matrix} \quad \begin{bmatrix} 1 & 1 & 1 & 0 & 4 \\ 0 & 1 & -4 & 5 & -7 \\ 0 & 0 & 1 & 8 & 21 \\ 0 & 0 & 0 & 11 & 22 \end{bmatrix}$$

# Lesson 14-7: Example

$$\begin{cases} 3u + 3v - \phantom{4}w = 1 \\ 4u - 2v + 4w = 3 \\ 5u + 8v - 2w = 2 \end{cases}$$

$$\begin{matrix} (R1): \\ (R2): \\ (R3): \end{matrix} \begin{bmatrix} 3 & 3 & -1 & 1 \\ 4 & -2 & 4 & 3 \\ 5 & 8 & -2 & 2 \end{bmatrix}$$

$$\begin{matrix} \\ -\frac{4}{3} \cdot (R1) + (R2): \\ \\ \end{matrix} \begin{bmatrix} 3 & 3 & -1 & 1 \\ 0 & -6 & \frac{16}{3} & \frac{5}{3} \\ 5 & 8 & -2 & 2 \end{bmatrix}$$

$$\begin{matrix} \\ \\ -\frac{5}{3} \cdot (R1) + (R3): \end{matrix} \begin{bmatrix} 3 & 3 & -1 & 1 \\ 0 & -6 & \frac{16}{3} & \frac{5}{3} \\ 0 & 3 & \frac{-1}{3} & \frac{1}{3} \end{bmatrix}$$

$$\begin{matrix} \\ \\ -\frac{1}{2} \cdot (R2) + (R3): \end{matrix} \begin{bmatrix} 3 & 3 & -1 & 1 \\ 0 & -6 & \frac{16}{3} & \frac{5}{3} \\ 0 & 3 & \frac{7}{3} & \frac{7}{6} \end{bmatrix}$$

$$\begin{matrix} \\ 3 \cdot (R2): \\ 6 \cdot (R3): \end{matrix} \begin{bmatrix} 3 & 3 & -1 & 1 \\ 0 & -18 & 16 & 5 \\ 0 & 0 & 14 & 7 \end{bmatrix}$$

# Lesson 14-8: Example

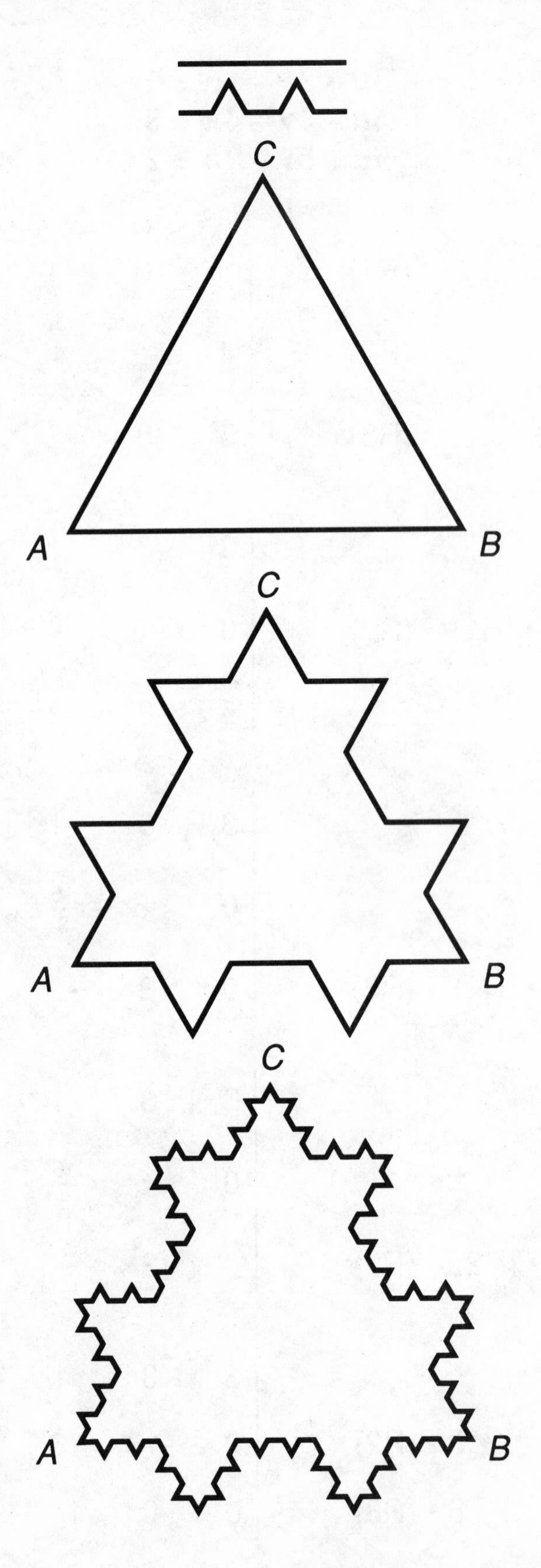